BITTERROOT

Jerry DeSanto

LERE PRESS

1993

DeSanto, Jerome S.
    Bitterrroot / Jerry DeSanto.
    p. cm.
    Includes bibliographical references and index.
    ISBN 0-9637889-0-6

    1. State flowers--Montana. 2. Tubers--West (U.S.) 3. Lewis and
Clark Expedition--(1804-1806)   I. Title.

QK85.3.M6D47 1993   583.152'0978
                                     QBI93-1227

Published by LERE Press, Babb, Montana
Layout by Creative Image, Missoula, Montana
Printed by Advanced Litho Printing, Great Falls, Montana
Cover artwork by Janet McGahan, Arlee, Montana
Cover design by Janet McGahan and David Rockwell, Arlee, Montana
To order copies, write author at P.O. Box 91, Babb, Montana 59411
A MONTANA PRODUCT

PREFACE AND ACKNOWLEDGMENTS

I first saw bitterroot in Yellowstone National Park in the early 1950s. In those years, and into the 1960s, I was a seasonal employee of the National Park Service. During the last few summers of those Yellowstone years, my supervisor was Wayne Replogle who had started his many summer seasons in Yellowstone back in the 1920s. Rep had an endless and consuming interest in everything related to the Indians of the Park area and together we made experiments with edible plants, jerky, pemmican and anything that could be even remotely connected with aboriginal food matters. Some of these experiments were disasters and, hence, inedible, including our efforts with bitterroot. As I now recall, some thirty years later, we took as our guide McDougall's and Bailey's *Plants of the Yellowstone National Park*. This otherwise excellent text stated that the roots of bitterroot were "boiled to a pink jelly" by Indians. We did that with messy and unpalatable results. Nevertheless, along the way, I learned much from Rep and my interest in plants and Indians continues. Rep is long gone as is his wife, Marian, but their friendship is one of my lasting memories of Yellowstone. This book is dedicated to them.

My attempt in what follows is to gather together everything I could learn and find on the subject of bitterroot. Therefore, this book is a record of my observations and conclusions, as well as a compilation of material from many sources. Some of these sources are readily available, but many are not, so I have included some little-known facts, legends, rumors and stories. I suppose I can be accused of what is said to be the exclusively American practice of including the results of all my research merely, as someone (probably a Britisher) has said, "to prove that it had been done". For this I blame my teachers of many years ago.

I ride the wave of enthusiasm for everything pertaining to the Lewis and Clark expedition and the two appendices reflect this interest. It is beyond me to explain why so many people are intrigued by the writings and the route of this famous adventure, but I know why I am. As I travel in the West, I always think of how it was when seen by the first white explorers. Of all early explorers, Meriwether Lewis and William Clark were the best. They saw the most, they reported on everything and their styles of expression are unforgettable.

This does not mean that they were the "discoverers" of anything new. They only reported, in the white man's way, on plants, animals, geography and other subjects that were all well-known to the Native Americans. I wish I knew far more than I do of the things known to the Native Americans of the early nineteenth century. I also vainly wish that I could see the land, its people and its products through the eyes of Lewis and Clark.

Recent finds of bitterroot in Alberta, where it had not been reported before 1982, have led to new theories on distribution and dispersal. These theories are locally controversial and I add my thoughts on these subjects believing they will continue to be argued.

Since moving to Glacier National Park in 1966, I have spent much time studying the flora of the Park and vicinity, particularly along the east front in Montana and Alberta. In 1989, I found bitterroot in Glacier (a first record for the Park) and soon after, friends and I found it in three new locations in and just east of the Park. Since then, curiosity about bitterroot has been the impetus for many trips and much research. Many people have helped and accompanied me and I particularly thank (in alphabetical order) Mrs. Zach Bugli for showing me the "yellow" bitterroot; Robin Cox who helped me count hundreds of bitterroot plants; Dave Dinwoodie for bringing sources to my attention; Bob Fry and Norma Craig for their efforts with *Lewisia disepala*; Henry Grant for much gardening information and for the gift of seeds of Watson's phase; H. D. Hampton who joined me on spring trips in the Bitterroot Valley and for the benefit of many discussions; Job Kuijt who gave me his views on bitterroot dispersal; Dick Mattson who found a new location and who has been my companion on many trips; Janet McGahan for graphic and creative art work; Jerry McGahan for help on some difficult text; Dave Rockwell who "computerized" the cover; Lucy Vanderburg for information on use of bitterroot by modern Flathead; John Vollertsen who reported a new location in Teton County, MT; Margaret Williams for information on *Lewisia maguirei*; Steve Wirt who sent me two articles and Rick Yates who told me of a new location in Glacier County, MT. Special thanks to Karen Feather who helped me at every stage of this project and encouraged me when I approached discouragement. Libraries in Montana, Idaho, Washington, Alberta and British Columbia have been helpful as have many correspondents in the United States and Canada. Thanks to Linda Rossi of the Academy of Natural Sciences in Philadelphia who found the unpublished Frederick Pursh material of 1812 for me. The assistance of United States Forest Service, United States Fish and Wildlife Service, Bureau of Land Management and National Park Service personnel throughout the West is acknowledged.

"flore maximo pulcherrime roseo." Sir William Jackson Hooker, 1863.

. . .

"I never see the Bitterroot blooming among the sage without feeling that I should take off my hat and stand in adoration of the wondrous skill of the creator." William O. Douglas, 1950.

. . .

"When I find the incomparable pale-rose blooms shining among the sage in June, I experience the same twinge I feel when, in similar lonely places, I come upon a bit of sun-purpled glass or a rusty, square-headed nail. Like these, the bitter root played a role in some of the lives of those who existed in the hundred years we soon celebrate." Harold Barnes, 1963.

. . .

"It is one of most beautiful flowers in all America. No other western wildling is richer in legend and tradition." Leonard Wiley, 1968.

. . .

"I shall never forget the sight of literally acres of sub-alpine turf sheeted with thousands of short-stemmed very large flowers of intense rose-red." Will Ingwersen, 1983.

Some readers have told me that Chapter 3 is a little dense for the non-botanist. Other readers with no botanical background find it challenging but comprehensible. In the interest of completeness, I leave it in place. I suppose it could be skipped over, but I do not recommend that.

The end notes are, in my opinion, absolutely necessary. I urge the serious reader to read them along with the appropriate text. Much of the detail found in the end notes is too specific to include in the text, but this detail is the essence of the story.

Contents

Illustrations

1
TRADITIONAL USE

EARLY NAMES AND USE

Long before white man first saw the bitterroot, the plant was well known and highly prized by native Americans. In Montana, Idaho, Washington and Oregon, it was a food plant of great significance. According to an early observer, the natives of the northwest (referring to southern British Columbia and Washington Territory in 1868) "look upon it as one of the great gifts from the Supreme Master of Life".[1] Among the roots gathered and eaten in the intermountain Pacific Northwest, only blue camas (*Camassia quamash*) and cous (*Lomatium cous*) were of similar value.

An early aboriginal name for the plant was *Petlum-asd-ilse-ne-mare*. The Flathead name was and is *spatlum* (variously rendered as *spitlum*, *spatulum* and *spoetlum*), the Snake name was *konah* (or *kana*) and the Kutenai name was *mepemcu*. Other aboriginal names include *chitah*, *lkupen*, *tlupen* and *eks-ix-ix*. The sign for bitterroot was the right index finger extended with the other fingers closed.[2]

The Flathead of the Bitterroot Valley in Montana were probably more closely associated with bitterroot than any other tribe. Two sets of stories relate to the place names of the Flathead's ancestral valley.

According to one account, the Flathead name for the river was *spitlem seulkn* meaning the water of the river of bitterroots. *Spitlemen*, or the place of the bitterroot, was the name of the valley.[3] Early trappers and hunters of French origin called the plant *racine amere*[4] (literally, bitter root) and applied the name to the geographical features of the valley. In time, translation from one or both languages resulted in the names of today.

In another story, today's Bitterroot River was called by the Flathead *In-schu-te-schu*, or Red Willow because of the shrubs, probably red-osier dogwood, that grew along the banks. The Bitterroot Mountains were known as *Chi-quil-quil-kane* or Red Mountains.[5] In this story there is no mention of the bitterroot plant.

The Snake Indians of the intermountain west made regular use of bitterroot, but little is known of their annual food quest. The Upper Kutenai from the area of the Tobacco Plains near Eureka, Montana and north into southern British Columbia also relied on bitterroot. Though the plant may have been known to them for only the last few hundred years,[6] it is reported to have been the most important root food in their repertory.[7] Other tribes south as far as California and down along the Rocky Mountains to Colorado made lesser use of bitterroot, but it must have been gathered every year where it grew in abundance. Bitterroot is most commonly found west of the continental divide. However, there are areas east of the divide, such as in south central Montana and in northern Yellowstone National Park, where the plant is locally common. Certainly these sites were annually harvested.

There is also the tradition that the Plains Indians, particularly the Blackfeet, raided or traded for the roots in the Bitterroot Valley. More common, however, was the practice of western Salishan tribes journeying to Montana bitterroot grounds to join in the harvest.

LEGENDS

Disagreement exists over how natives learned of bitterroot. Duncan McDonald, an early informant whose knowledge extended well back into the nineteenth century, stated there was no legend of its origin among the Flathead.[8] Nevertheless, stories are told of how these natives came to know bitterroot.

A starving old woman, one legend goes, was comforted by a red bird, an emissary from the sun. The bird spoke to the old woman:

> A new plant will be formed from your sorrowful tears
> which have fallen into the soil. Its flower will have the rose
> of my wing feathers and the white of your hair. It will have
> leaves close to the ground. Your people will eat the roots
> of this plant. Though it will be bitter from your sorrow, it
> will be good for them. When they see these flowers, they
> will say "Here is the silver of our mother's hair upon the
> ground and the rose from the wings of the spirit bird. Our
> mother's tears of bitterness have given us food."[9]

The "white" and "silver" apparently refer to the white and hair-like stamens and pistils of some flowers and also could describe the relatively common white phase of the bitterroot. Flowers of pale rose color also have a silvery caste.

In another legend of origin, the finding of bitterroot is attributed to Coyote, the chief culture hero of the Salishan people.[10] Told by Pierre Pichette, the story describes how, long before the appearance of man on earth, the starving Coyote found a field of pink flowers, pulled up some, peeled the roots and experimentally tasted them. He found the raw roots too bitter so he cooked them in a cleverly contrived oven until they were well done and tender. Coyote declared that the roots "saved me from starvation." Presumably referring to the Bitterroot Valley, he said, "Here in this valley where I have feasted, these bitter roots will grow abundantly. At this season when the skin peels easily from the root, the human beings will dig the roots as I have done."[11]

The similarities in the two stories suggest that bitterroot was used first by the Salish as an emergency food. Its desirable qualities were then discovered and it became a staple of their diet.

The Upper Kutenai explained the plant's origin by a story involving an unsatisfactory marriage. An Upper Kutenai brave traveled south, presumably to Flathead territory, and married a woman, taking her north with him. In her baggage were camas and bitterroot roots. She did not like the country up north and returned to her homeland. Along the way, she discarded the roots and they revived and spread.[12] This is why both plants are found in the land of the Upper Kutenai.

BITTERROOT COLLECTING

Among the natives of western Montana, the time of bitterroot harvesting was an annual event of great sociability and much significance. In the Bitterroot Valley, the resident Flathead were joined by other Salishan tribes during the "Bitterroot Month," the fifth lunar month of the year.

Though accounts vary, it seems that the optimum time for gathering bitterroot was in May. The distinctive basal leaves of the plant were then easily recognizable and buds would be well developed. The natives were aware that roots were less bitter then than later. They also must have known that the roots contained more starch then than at any other time, though at the same time root sugar levels were declining.[13] Bitterroot was valued for starch and not for sugar. The root of blue camas, berries and the inner bark of certain trees were among the vegetable sources that satisfied the craving for sweets.

Certain areas were believed to produce better tasting roots than others. The natives flocked to these areas, set up temporary camps and turned to the serious business of root gathering.

It was entirely feminine work and, among the Flathead, older women officiated at a "First Roots Ceremony." This was observed as the first day of harvest and it was thought that if the ceremony were not held, the roots would be small and scarce. Furthermore, no other species of plant could be

Bitterroot just before bloom. Roots were
harvested when plants were at this stage.

harvested until the successful conclusion of the "First Roots Ceremony."
No other plant — neither camas, cous nor any of the berries — was, as Harry
Turney-High wrote, "so honored".[14] A small amount of roots was gathered
and a portion was distributed to every member of the encampment.[15] The
harvest then commenced, usually continuing for about a week, until enough
was collected to last until the next season. This amount was one to two
bushels for each family.

Flathead Encampment near Missoula at Bitterroot Time, c. 1920. (UM Archives)

Mourning Dove, a Salishan author who lived in eastern Washington, has left a description of the collection and use of bitterroot. Her recollections are undated, but probably refer to experiences of the 1890s or early 1900s.

> Often we went to Okanagan country to gather Bitterroot (spit-lum), which grew abundantly on the sagebrush flats close to the Okanagan River. The women dug up this plant with pointed dogwood digging sticks, called pee-cha . . . The thin, twisted roots are dug when the plant is in bud, they are peeled immediately while they remain moist.[16]

One writer stated that bitterroot "was dug here [in Montana] by the Indians in great quantities for uncounted centuries, yet it was never diminished".[17] Another account describes how bitterroot roots were dug and how primitive, but probably effective measures were taken to prevent depletion or extermination.

> The plant was dug out by trenching the earth about four or five inches from the plant. Lift the earth and pull out the plant, simultaneously, the entire four to six inch root will come out unharmed. Knock the dirt off, back into the hole, top the plant by pulling at the leaves and buds until they separate from the root. Break a section of the red, root skin at the crown of the root and strip it down. Throw the plant, buds and skin back into the hole, to grow again.[18]

The regenerative part of the plant is in the crown (actually the caudex), at the apex of the root. If it were replanted, however carelessly, many plants would grow, flower and develop new root systems.

For obvious reasons, small immature plants would not be harvested so they would be spared. Also, in areas of particular abundance and ready germination (such as in the Bitterroot Valley), growth of new plants would compensate for the loss due to annual harvest.

Native Americans probably practiced conservation in most, if not all, of their plant harvesting techniques. Bitterroot, as an example, was not severely diminished by the annual gathering at select sites by relatively few users. The chief cause for the loss of bitterroot across its original range has been and is the loss of habitat. This loss is the inevitable result of settlement, industrialization, the development of commercial sites and the continuing expansion of suburban and rural housing complexes. In the Bitterroot Valley, these changes began in the mid-nineteenth century and they continue today. Harvesting by a few thousand people over a large area for many centuries had only a negligible effect.

Flathead Indians gathering bitterroot roots. Note digging tool in foreground. (Ernst Peterson, Ravalli County Museum, Hamilton, MT)

One of the better-known digging grounds was north of Hamilton, Montana, at the so-called "Dancing Place." Another was near Fort Missoula, referred to as the "greatest of all" and owing at least some of its fame to the favored campsite at the cold spring named *Stil-at-coo*.[19] The site of the University of Montana and the flats just south of the campus were also well-known digging grounds. During the bitterroot season, tepee camps were pitched on the flats into the 1930s.[20]

To the north, the Tobacco Plains and the valley of the Little Bitterroot River were regularly harvested by the Upper Kutenai. Farther north still and at the northern extremity of its range, bitterroot was collected in the area of Fort Steele, British Columbia.[21]

Before flowering, the roots were not only high in starch and less bitter than later in the season, but the unpalatable bark of the roots was also easily slipped off. The bitterest part of the plant, the orange-colored living periderm beneath the bark, also was easily removed at this time. The core of the root, also known as the stele, was excised by some as it was believed that it was another undesirably bitter element. One reported belief is that this core was "the heart" of the plant "and you must not eat it because it is sacred".[22]

A strong tradition, still current, indicates that something of value was offered to the spirits in return for the bounty of bitterroot roots.[23] This may have been a simple small item, such as a bead, placed in the hole after the removal of the first root.[24] Or it may have been tobacco or in later years, a coin. This offering also was made when other roots (blue camas, for instance) were dug.

BITTERROOT AS FOOD

"It is one of the marvels in the history of alimentation that the unappetizing roots of this plant, intensely bitter when raw and smelling like tobacco when boiling, should have secured a stable place in any human bill of fare."[25] The bitterness of bitterroots has long been a subject of interest to samplers. Meriwether Lewis, in a frequently quoted passage, found the dried and boiled roots "naucious to my pallate" on 22 August 1805.[26] David Thompson wrote of "a white root of slightly bitter taste which becomes a favourite, and is agreeable to the stomach." He called the root "Ka-mass" in 1847 (after sampling it in 1811) though his description applies more closely to the peeled root of bitterroot than it does to the root of blue camas. It is likely that after thirty-six years he confused the bitterroot root with the name of camas.[27] In 1865, Granville Stuart wrote that the roots had "an exceedingly bitter taste" so that he "never could eat it unless very hungry." He did acknowledge, however, that "many of the mountaineers are very fond of it".[28] In 1876, Montana pioneer W. A. Clark announced that though bitterroot was important to the Indians, the roots "are wholly unsavory to the more refined palate".[29] In the late nineteenth century, Dr. Valery Havard, an army surgeon, wrote that the "brownish-red bark is intensely bitter while the inner white and farinaceous part is quite palatable and nutritious, although having in the raw state a slight bitterish flavor. Boiled or otherwise cooked they are excellent food."[30] Montana botanist and professor Morton J. Elrod noted that cooking bitterroot converts it to a palatable food, but he echoed W. A. Clark when he added "at least to an Indian's taste".[31] This popular view was put in another way by a chemist and wildflower expert who wrote that "even after removal of the intensely bitter, orange-coloured, inner bark, the white interior pulp remains rather unpalatable to the European taste".[32] Many other comments from the nineteenth and twentieth centuries could be cited. Most of them describe the unacceptable bitterness of bitterroot roots. A modern sampler, after trying several preparations, concluded that "it was bitter no matter how prepared or served".[33]

Another current view seems to be closer to the truth. This opinion is that of a student of bitterroot and a persistent experimenter. "On many occasions I have tasted the fresh roots of Lewisia [bitterroot] and I have never sensed more than a faint bitterness after masticating it for a time," wrote Rexford Daubenmire. "However, I have detected a definite bitterness after boiling dried roots in water for some time."[34] This is completely at odds with the view of ethnologist James A. Teit who wrote that the roots are "palatable only after cooking because of too much bitterness in the raw state".[35] A tolerance for whatever bitterness there may be is probably an acquired taste, said Duncan McDonald, "like learning to use tobacco".[36]

Much has been written about the preparation and serving of bitterroot roots. There seems to be little record of consumption of fresh roots though in times of necessity, some would have been eaten readily. During the harvest, some must have been sampled. One problem with eating fresh roots is the resultant swelling of the stomach if more than a little is consumed. This could lead to acute discomfort.[37] Lewis and Clark graphically described unpleasant results from eating roots. Most of their problems, however, occurred after eating blue camas roots.

Bitterroot roots were peeled after digging, sometimes washed, and then dried in the sun. They were kept dry until use. Contrary to some reports, cooking generally consisted of only a few minutes of steaming. This was often done on a lattice of twigs over a kettle of water.[38] Two accounts tell of boiling the roots "to a pink jelly,"[39,] but this seems to result only in a completely useless mess.

Peeled roots of bitterroot before drying.

After cooking, the roots were eaten plain, served with meat as a stew, or sweetened with berries or prepared blue camas roots. In 1846, botanist Charles Geyer described a stew made with bitterroot roots and the marrow of bison bones. It was, he wrote, "the most dainty dish . . . a very wholesome food".[40] After the availability of commercial sweetening, cooked roots were served with molasses or sugar. Bitterroot apparently furnished much of the carbohydrate needed in some early diets. The roots had good keeping qualities, needing only to be kept dry to last indefinitely. Since roots gathered at the proper time were not woody, they did not become tough or stringy in storage or in cooking.

Early accounts made exaggerated claims of the nutritive value of bitterroot roots. These claims have been repeated often and some are still believed. William Jackson Hooker, the eminent British botanist, wrote in 1830 that the roots "are admirably calculated for carrying on long journeys; two or three per day being sufficient for a man, even while undergoing great fatigue".[41] Hooker had his information from David Douglas who had collected bitterroot in the northwestern United States in the 1820s. Hooker's report was repeated, almost verbatim, by Robert Brown to the Botanical Society of Edinburgh in 1868.[42] Dr. Edwin Palmer, writing in 1870, said that bitterroot "abounds in concentrated nutriment, a single ounce of the dried article being sufficient for a meal".[43] This latter claim was contested by Havard in 1895 who described Palmer as a "too credulous observer".[44] Bitterroot undoubtedly supplies starchy carbohydrate in good quantity, but it would be impossible for a few ounces daily to nourish an active person. The nutrients in bitterroot are reported to be "similar to those in brown rice except it is lower in iron and higher in calcium and phosphorous".[45]

Charles Geyer, when writing of his western adventures of 1843 and 1844, told a story about the value of bitterroot roots that has been repeated many times. He wrote that a sackful of roots "commands generally the price of a good horse".[46] This comment was analyzed many years later and found to be "not very illuminating, as sacks, like pieces of chalk, vary in size, and horses in worthwhileness".[47]

MODERN INDIAN USE

The Flatheads visited the bitterroot grounds along the Bitterroot River well into the twentieth century, but these journeys are no longer made. Professor J. E. Kirkwood wrote in 1916, "every spring the Indians may still be seen gathering them [bitterroot roots] on the plains about Missoula".[48] Encampments near the grounds of the University of Montana were annual spring events and Harry Turney-High lamented the declining visits in 1933:

> For with every recurring bitter root season, we notice fewer and fewer tipis pitched on the flats south of the university. The culture of the Salish is passing, along with their grand old men, whose descendants are not content to be Men Without Machines. The rapid diffusion of the easy Woolworth-pot-and-pan complex has perhaps made the following cooking method impossible ever to see again.

[Turney-High goes on to describe methods for cooking bitterroot and blue camas].[49]

In the 1940s, Leonard Wiley watched an aged Salishan woman dig bitterroot. She had dug bitterroot at the same location for about seventy-five years. Her tools were an iron rod about two feet long with a wood cross bar and a pointed stick about eight inches long. She dug the roots with the rod twice as fast as Wiley could with modern tools. She used the awl stick to remove bits of bark from the roots. In this way, she could gather two gunny sacksful in a week.

Wiley observed that the old people did legendary routines "skillfully and easily", but they could not cope with newness.[50] So when their traditional bitterroot grounds, for instance, were lost to changes wrought by white man's culture, they were unable or unwilling to adapt to new practices or places.

Dorothy Johnson wrote of a visit to a bitterroot camp in 1953. The tent camp was set up a few miles southwest of Missoula and was occupied by the Big Sam family and 83-year-old Sophie Moiese of Arlee, Montana. One of the Big Sams was a Blackfeet and though she liked to eat the roots, she reported that the people from the Blackfeet Reservation east of the mountains used them only as a medicine and specifically to check hemorrhages.[51] This use apparently is continued by some Blackfeet today.

Pilgrimages to the Bitterroot Valley persisted until the 1960s. One account stated that the digs "lasted until a year or so ago [written in 1963] in dwindling fashion, when the group of older Indians and the few sympathetic younger ones who marshalled near Missoula for the annual affair announced it was the last".[52] Sporadic sentimental visits may still occur, but suburban development has exterminated the bitterroot in many of the old sites near Missoula.[53]

In the spring of 1971, Mary Ann Combs, described as "one of the last of the original Bitterroot Valley Salish," gathered bitterroot in the Stevensville, Montana area. Her visit was in company with Margaret Sullivan of the local historical society. After digging the first root, Mrs. Combs "thanked the Lord [but which Lord?] for the food," dug a supply and cleaned them. The roots were prepared by steaming for about twenty minutes. According to Mrs. Sullivan, the roots were "pungent and distinctive, not bitter".[54]

Organized digging for bitterroot is still done in the vicinity of St. Ignatius, Montana. This seems to be the remaining stronghold of traditional knowledge and practices among the Flathead. The first roots (or first fruits) ceremony is still observed and the roots are harvested in quantity in early May. Modern adaptations include the use of crafted steel digging tools and the storage of roots in freezers.[55]

In eastern Washington, bitterroot is still gathered for food and as recently as 1990, it was described as "an important if limited part of the Colville diet, served at all meals with a religious purpose, whether Catholic or traditional, especially modern versions of the First Food rites." Modern cooking methods include preparation with orange-flavored gelatine.[56] Another modern cooking use is reported from the Blackfeet Reservation. According to Bob Scriver, bitterroot is still "of importance to the Blackfeet" and he mentions its use in service berry soup. The ingredients in this soup are beef ribs to make a broth, serviceberries, sugar, flour, and bitterroot roots. The soup is described as "very filling and nutritious" and presumably is still made east of the mountains during ceremonies.[57]

The roots are prized as food, but dietary satisfaction is not the only reason for their consumption. There is a belief the bitterroot roots are a good and healthy food and that they furnish some spiritual, as well as physical, benefit. In the old days, there seemed to be no record of its use as a tonic or a medicine, but in modern times, some Flathead apparently have adopted the Cree practice of boiling the roots in water and drinking the decoction. Reportedly, the potion eases the pain of heart trouble and pleurisy.[58] It also is stated that some of the older people chewed the finely ground roots as a soothing medicine for sore throats.[59]

It is unclear if traditional Blackfeet used bitterroot as food, though it seems likely they would have done so on an irregular basis.[60] Some trading by modern Blackfeet with Flatheads continues, but most of the Blackfeet use of bitterroot is medicinal. Though the earliest known name for bitterroot in the Blackfeet language was *Eks-ix-ix,*[61] that name now seems to be lost. The current name is reported as *Est tsi kopo.*[62]

ENDNOTES

1. R. Brown, p. 381.

2. The various names are listed by R. Brown, p. 381; Daubenmire, p. 10; Bitterroot Trails, I, p. 26 and McClintock, p. 530. Johnston, p. 34, mentions the sign. Saunders, p. 27, apparently alone, says *spatlum* "really means tobacco". This is inaccurate.

3. Wheeler, 2, p. 76. Harold Barnes wrote that "the Salish referred to all the land between the divide and what is now Idaho as *Spelemen* — 'the place of the bitterroot'". *Helena Independent Record*, Dec. 29, 1963, MHS Folder.

4. There is some confusion over the common name *racine amere*. In 1846, Charles Geyer applied it to both bitterroot and a species of valerian. Geyer, p. 298.

5. Murray, p. 13-14.

6. The Kutenai may have "originated" east of the mountains where there is little or no bitterroot. Schaeffer, p. 62.

7. Turney-High, *Kutenai*, p. 33.

8. Murray, p. 5. Though McDonald lived among the Flathead, his native heritage was Nez Perce.

9. E. Clark, p. 168.

10. The Salish language stock includes the Flathead and Pend d'Oreille (primarily), Kalispell, Coeur d'Alene, Spokane, Columbia, Wenatchee, and Coast Salishan tribes.

11. Pichette, p. 30-33.

12. Hart, p. 47.

13. Starch level in May is about 40%. Marvel, p. 101-102.

14. Turney-High, *Flathead*, p. 34.

15. Stubbs, p. 62.

16. Mourning Dove, p. 19.

17. Murray, p. 40.

18. Bitterroot Trails, I, p. 26.

19. Murray, p. 11.

20. Turney-High, *Cooking*, p. 1.

21. Turney-High, *Kutenai*, p. 33.

22. Johnson, *Great Falls Tribune*, June 14, 1953, MHS Folder.

23. Vanderburg, May 17, 1991.

24. Malouf note, 1991.

25. Duboc article, p. 427, p. 444, MHS Folder.

26. Thwaites, 3, p. 13, although Kim Williams wrote (mistakenly) that Lewis and Clark "ate bitterroot enthusiastically". Williams, 1972.

27. Thompson, p. 291.

28. Stuart, p. 57.

29. W. A. Clark, p. 55.

30. Havard, p. 111. Also, Lemmon and Johnson, p. 121.

31. Elrod, n. p.

32. L. Clark, p. 120.

33. Duncan, p. 294-5.

34. Daubenmire, p. 11.

35. Teit, p. 478. The results of my experiments agree with those of Daubenmire.

36. Quoted in Murray, p. 9.

37. Duboc article, p . 427, MHS Folder.

38. Hart, p. 80; Stubbs, p. 63.

39. McDougall and Baggley, p. 73. Charles Geyer had mentioned the same cooking process many years earlier. Geyer, p. 307.

40. Geyer, p. 307. Another report notes that whatever bitterness remained after boiling was not noticeable when the roots were used in soups and stews. Scully, n. d., Diettert File.

41. Hooker, 1830, p. 34.

42. R. Brown, p. 381.

43. Palmer, p. 407. These claims accepted by Murray, p. 10.

44. Havard, p. 111.

45. Walker, p. 184.

46. Quoted in *Range Plant Handbook*, p. W165.

47. Saunders, p. 27.

48. Kirkwood, p. 46.

49. Turney-High, *Cooking*, p. 1. Turney-High goes into detail regarding the cooking of bitterroot and camas, but according to Stubbs (who does not cite his authority), he probably witnessed neither cooking nor gathering of these roots. Stubbs, p. 7.

50. Wiley, p. 263-5.

51. Johnson, *Great Falls Tribune*, June 14, 1953, MHS Folder.

52. Barnes, *Helena Independent Record*, Dec. 29, 1963, MHS Folder.

53. The suburban development in the Miller Creek area near Missoula has caused the loss of much of one of the best old bitterroot sites.

54. Stevensville Historical Society, p. 5 note.

55. Vanderburg, May 17, 1991. See also "Salish Indians honor bitterroot as first fruit" by Bill Turner, *Ronan Pioneer*, May 6, 1987.

56. According to Jay Miller, editor, Mourning Dove, p. 200 note.

57. Scriver, p. 34; p. 261.

58. Stubbs, p. 105.

59. Scully, n. d., Diettert File.

60. McClintock states that the Blackfeet believed it was "healthy food". He also wrote that "It [bitterroot] grows plentifully in the mountains" although he gives no locations, p. 530.

61. McClintock, p. 530. McClintock lived among the Blackfeet for periods of time beginning in 1896 and wrote of them in 1910. Name repeated in Johnston, p. 34.

62. Shaw, K. & L., 1992. Letter from.

2
HISTORY

LEWIS AND CLARK

Captain Meriwether Lewis.
Portrait by Charles Wilson Peale.

Captain Meriwether Lewis tasted the root of bitterroot in August of 1805. This was the first known experience of white man with the plant, but at the time Lewis knew only that the root was too bitter for his taste and that the Indians (in this case, Shoshone) "eat them heartily".[1] In 1893 Elliott Coues stated that the roots tasted by Lewis were of the bitterroot plant, and this determination was unquestionably accurate.[2] The clue to the identification was the description of the root in Lewis's journal of 22 August 1805:

> Another speceis was much mutilated but appeared to be fibrous; the parts were brittle, hard of the size of a small quill, cilindric and white as snow throughout, except some

parts of the hard black rind which they had not seperated in
the preservation. this the Indians with me informed were
always boiled for use. I made the experiment, found that
they became perfectly soft by boiling, but had a very bitter
taste . . .³

On their return trip in 1806, the Lewis and Clark expedition camped on
what they called Travellers rest Creek near its junction with their Clark's
River. These two streams are now known as Lolo Creek and the Bitterroot
River.⁴ This was a favored campsite with good grass, water, wood, and game
and had been used on the westbound journey in September of 1805. The
party arrived at Travellers rest on June 30 and departed on July 3. During
that time, Lewis collected bitterroot in flower, as well as several other new
species of plants. Whether he knew that the flower he collected was of the
same species he had tasted in 1805 is unknown. Probably he did.

The bitterroot was collected at or very near the mouth of Lolo Creek.⁵
Lewis's only mention in his journal of such a striking plant as bitterroot was
that it was one of "several other uncommon plants specemines of which I
preserved".⁶ Coues has pointed out that if Lewis and Clark commented
specifically and in detail on plants in their journals, the plants usually do not
appear in the preserved collections.⁷ Recently, it has been said that when
Lewis collected and preserved a plant, he wrote little or nothing about it in
his journal.⁸ These peculiarities are usually consistent, but there are exceptions. One such exception was the collection of ragged robin (*Clarkia
pulchella*) by Lewis on 1 June 1806 followed by a detailed description of
the same plant in his journal.⁹ Bitterroot is an example of a collection that
has only slight mention in the journals; the more detailed description of
another new species, mountain lady slipper (*Cypripedium montanum*), was
not accompanied by a collection. This spectacular orchid was seen on 30
June 1806 and the description appears in Lewis's journal of that date and
Clark's journal of 2 July 1806.¹⁰

Lewis's discovery of bitterroot on July 1 was possible only because the
growing season of 1806 was very late. In the vicinity of the type collection,¹¹
wild bitterroot typically sets seeds by late June. Only rarely will any but
cultivated plants be in bloom past the middle of June. The finding of
mountain lady slipper in bloom at the end of June is another indication of
the lateness of the season, as is the depth of snow recorded by Clark in his
weather diary of 17 June 1806:

. . . on the 17th at meridian [Lolo Pass], the Snow became
so deep in every derection from 6 to 8 feet deep we could
not prosue the road.¹²

After leaving Travellers rest, both Lewis's party and Clark's party were soon out of "bitterroot country" so only climatic chance led to the discovery of what has been described as "the most celebrated of all plants brought back by Lewis".[13]

In his brief note on the sheet accompanying the collected bitterroot, Lewis did not mention the color of the bitterroot petals. Eight years later, when the species finally was described and published, the type description noted that the flowers were white. Over a century later, a journalist reported that the type flowers retained "faint traces of their original dawn-rose color".[14] Paul Russell Cutright examined Lewis's dried bitterroot collection in 1966 and wrote that it consisted of "six somewhat faded flowers" — all that remained of Lewis's original "low perennial bearing beautiful rose-colored flowers".[15] Allowing for journalistic speculation by the *Missoulian* and for uncharacteristic confusion by Cutright, the original flowers were certainly white.[16] White-flowered bitterroot are not as common as the red phase, but they are by no means rare. Red-flowered bitterroot collections tend to fade in time, but no dried red flowers fade to total white.

437. LEWISIA. *Pursh in linn. trans. v.* 11.

Lewisia. *l. c.*
On the banks of Clarck's river. ♃. July. *v. s. in Herb. Lewis.* Petals white ; calyx elegantly red-veined, of a consistency like paper.
Radix fusiformis, ramosa, sanguinea. *Folia* radicalia linearia, subcarnosa, obtusiuscula. *Scapus* uniflorus ? an biflorus. *Pedicellus* basi geniculatus. *Calyx* coloratus, scariosus, 7—9-phyllus, patens : foliolis ovatis, acutis, concavis, nervoso-venosis, interioribus angustioribus. *Petala* 14—18. alba, lanceolata, patentia, calyce vix duplo longiora. *Filamenta* 14—18. receptaculo petalis opposite inserta, filiformia, calyce breviora. *Antheræ* oblongæ, erectæ. *Germen* superum, ovatum, glabrum. *Stylus* filiformis, staminibus paulo longior, superne trifidus. *Stigmata* 3. bifida. *Capsula* oblonga, 3-locularis : loculis bispermis. *Semina* lenticularia, nitida, nigra.
This elegant plant would be a very desirable addition to the ornamental perennials, since, if once introduced, it would be easily kept and propagated, as the following circumstance will clearly prove. The specimen with roots taken out of the Herbarium of M. Lewis, Esq. was planted by Mr. M'Mahon of Philadelphia, and vegetated for more than one year : but some accident happening to it, I had not the pleasure of seeing it in flower.

First published description of Lewisia rediviva *(bitterroot) from F. Pursh,* Flora Americae Septentrionalis, *1814.*

Lewis, who had some botanical training and was a dedicated field naturalist,[17] collected plants under trying circumstances. Not only was he required to press and dry his plants (in much the same way modern field botanists do) under primitive conditions, but also it was of paramount importance to keep the plants dry as he continued his often arduous travels. In 1806 the great difficulty was transportation. The bitterroot collected on 1 July 1806, for example, traveled 3000 miles by horse, boat and stagecoach before reaching Philadelphia in early 1807.

Before arriving in Philadelphia, Lewis received a letter from Bernard McMahon, a well-known horticulturist and seed merchant in that city. McMahon encouraged Lewis to consider the qualifications of an acquaintance, "a very intelligent and practical Botanist, who would be well inclined to render you any service in his power".[18] The botanist was Frederick Pursh, a German educated in Dresden and who had been in the United States since 1799. He had collected for Benjamin Smith Barton, Lewis's botanical mentor, and though it appears he was not personally admired, he was widely respected as a field botanist and taxonomist. Many years later, Pursh was accurately described as the "most logical and careful botanist of his time dealing with our American plants".[19]

Lewis delivered some of his dried plants to McMahon and Pursh in April of 1807. Included in this group of plants, many new, was the 1 July 1806 collection of bitterroot. Lewis's label accompanying the six bitterroot plants read "The Indians eat the root of this. Near Clark's River, July 1, 1806."[20] Thus ended Meriwether Lewis's connection with the results of the famous expedition. His appointment in 1807 as governor of Louisiana led, as Cutright wrote, to "innumerable frustrating administrative problems . . . and the enforced sedentary existence inimitable to health".[21] His premature and tragic death followed in October of 1809. Lewis had not been able to make even the slightest progress on his assigned task of writing up the history of the expedition. This history had been planned to include a full account of scientific discoveries and natural history.

McMAHON AND PURSH

When McMahon examined Lewis's bitterroot collections he noticed signs of new growth. The roots with crowns were then severed from the flowering stems and planted. In 1814, seven years later, Pursh wrote that the planted roots "vegetated for more than a year, but some accident happening to it, I had not the pleasure of seeing it in flower".[22] The plant never did flower, although a modern annotator says the roots "grew and produced flowers when removed from the collection of dried specimens".[23] It is more likely that the transplants perished in the damp and inhospitable climate of Philadelphia long before flowering. Favorable growing conditions for bitterroot require a combination of soil, temperature and moisture that leads to physiological inactivity following the blooming period. McMahon was an experienced plantsman, but he was either unaware of these requirements or was unable to simulate them.

Aside from a collecting trip to the West Indies, Pursh was variously employed in Philadelphia and New York until he moved to London in 1811. During the 1807-1811 period, the mangled collection of Lewis's bitterroot, now reduced to flowers and stems, was probably in McMahon's care. Pursh did not take the bitterroot collections with him to London although he did take thirty-nine other specimens of Lewis and Clark plants.[24] He must have been well supplied with notes and sketches of the material left behind. Though he did not specify, Pursh himself wrote that he had returned to London in 1811 "with an ample stock of materials towards a FLORA OF NORTH AMERICA".[25] There were now two sets of Lewis and Clark plants; one in Philadelphia and one in London. Both were soon to drop from sight for more than eighty years.

When Pursh arrived in London, armed with some of Lewis's specimens and with notes regarding those in Philadelphia, he immediately began work on what was to be his *Flora Americae Septentrionalis*, to be subtitled:

> or, A Systematic Arrangement and Description of the Plants of North America. Containing, Besides what May Have Been Described By Preceeding Authors; Many New and Rare Species, Collected During Twelve Years Travel and Residence in that Country.

Flora Americæ Septentrionalis;

OR, A

SYSTEMATIC ARRANGEMENT

AND

D E S C R I P T I O N

OF

THE PLANTS

OF

NORTH AMERICA.

CONTAINING, BESIDES WHAT HAVE BEEN DESCRIBED BY
PRECEDING AUTHORS, MANY NEW AND RARE
SPECIES, COLLECTED DURING TWELVE
YEARS TRAVELS AND RESIDENCE
IN THAT COUNTRY,

BY

FREDERICK PURSH.

IN TWO VOLUMES.

WITH TWENTY-FOUR ENGRAVINGS.

VOL. II.

LONDON:

PRINTED FOR WHITE, COCHRANE, AND CO.,
FLEET STREET.

1814.

Title page, Pursh, Flora Americae
Septentrionalis, *1814.*

The work was completed during the winter of 1811-12 (but not published until 1814) when Pursh, a man of intemperate habits, "was kept under lock and key with carefully restricted fluid stimulation, and allowed an hour's walk a day, under guard, to insure his return to his labors".[26]

As far back as 1807, when he first saw the plants brought east by Lewis, Pursh knew he was seeing new and hitherto unknown material. In his *Flora*, he eventually described four new genera from the collection of the expedition. One was bitterroot, which he named *Lewisia rediviva*.[27] The genus name commemorates Captain Lewis and the specific epithet refers to McMahon's experience with the remarkable reviving power of seemingly dead plants. *Rediviva* is perhaps best translated as "restored to life". On the type herbarium sheet, Pursh copied Lewis's brief description accompanying the dried plants and added "the calyx consists of 6 or 7 leaves, the corolla many petals and stamens [word undecipherable] capsule".[28] In *Flora Americae Septentrionalis*, he changed the spelling of Clark to Clarck and noted that the petals were white and the calyx "elegantly red-veined." Bitterroot would be a "very desirable addition to the ornamental perennials," Pursh wrote, and cited McMahon's temporary success cultivating the dried roots.[29]

Flora Americae Septentrionalis, in two volumes, "was admirably executed" and "in breadth of treatment, exceeded anything heretofore written about the North American flora".[30] One hundred and twenty -four Lewis and Clark plants were described and thirteen were illustrated. Unfortunately, *Lewisia* was not illustrated, indicating that Pursh did not have the plant with him in London. Thomas Nuttall commented on this omission in 1818 when he asked, "was it not of more importance to have given a figure of this very interesting plant [bitterroot] than of *Monarda Kalmiana* or *Lupinus villosus*"?[31]

Although Pursh did not illustrate bitterroot in his *Flora*, he apparently had drawn sketches of Lewis's plants before January of 1812. At that time, four papers taken from Pursh's yet unpublished *Flora* were read before the Linnean Society in London, but none were published. One of these papers, "Four new genera of Plants," was based on Pursh's descriptions of *Lewisia*,[32] *Clarkia*, *Calochortus* and *Tigarea*. One version of the text of this paper included drawings of bitterroot, and this paper, with the drawings, survives

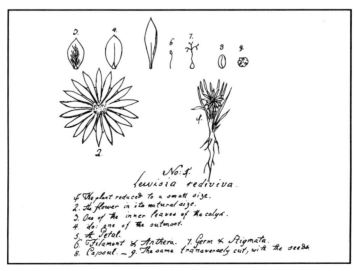

Pursh's unpublished drawing and brief description of
Lewisia rediviva *(bitterroot), 1812.*

in manuscript.[33] As early as May of 1807, Lewis had paid Pursh $30 "for assisting me in preparing drawings and arranging specemines of plants for my work." In the same month, he paid Pursh an additional $40 "in advance" for the preparation of drawings.[34] In January of 1809, McMahon wrote to Jefferson that Pursh had been in McMahon's house "upward of twelve months drawing and describing his [Lewis's] plants, which he left with me [McMahon] for that purpose".[35] It must have been one of these drawings done in Philadelphia that eventually formed part of the paper read before the Linnean Society in 1812.

Pursh traveled to Canada soon after the completion of his *Flora* and there he died, destitute, in 1820. He was only 46.[36] Whatever his faults (and he was much maligned in the nineteenth century), he was scrupulously fair in crediting Lewis and Clark and in carefully transcribing their notes. His possible but unproven complicity in the casual treatment of the type specimen of *Lewisia rediviva* would be inexcusable today, but in those days it seemed accepted practice.

HOOKER AND 19TH CENTURY COLLECTORS

Since Pursh did not include an illustration of bitterroot in his *Flora* and since the Linnean Society manuscript had little or no circulation, European knowledge of the species relied solely on his brief written description. In 1830, William Jackson Hooker wrote that he was unaware of any herbarium specimens of bitterroot in Europe.[37] David Douglas had collected flowering bitterroot plants in 1826, but had lost them. Hooker went on to say that Douglas had collected more plants, but without flowers, in March of 1827, "on the banks of some of the tributary streams of the Columbia." Some of these plants were brought to London and planted in the garden of the London Horticultural Society. "But," wrote Hooker, "like those at Philadelphia, they vegetated for a short time, and then perished".[38]

At the same time, Thomas Drummond was collecting in the area of the Canadian Rockies east of the continental divide. In his travels he acquired dried roots and plants of a species unknown to him and sent them on to Hooker. According to Hooker, Drummond reported that Indians west of the mountains used them as food. The roots were, as Hooker wrote, "well known to the Canadian hunters, and to the officers of the Hudson's Bay Company".[39] Though Hooker's account is somewhat ambiguous, it seems there was trans-divide trade in these roots at least as early as the 1820s.

While at London, Douglas determined that Drummond's collection was of the same species as the *Lewisia* of Pursh. Specimens with leaves and buds were immersed in hot water to rehydrate them and sketches were made.

These sketches and Hooker's Latin description appear in Hooker's article of 1830. Drummond's plants were undoubtedly the bitterroot of Pursh. The only point of difference was the root. Hooker described Drummond's collection as having white roots whereas Pursh's plants were "*sanguinea*" (blood-colored).[40] Hooker explained this later when he realized that Drummond's collections " .. . were imperfect [peeled, hence white], from having been prepared for food".[41] The roots described by Pursh were still covered with the dark colored bark and periderm. Additionally, Douglas's lost plants had rose-colored flowers, compared to the white of Pursh's, but Hooker rightly made little of this difference.[42] Hooker also had seen excellent dried specimens collected by William

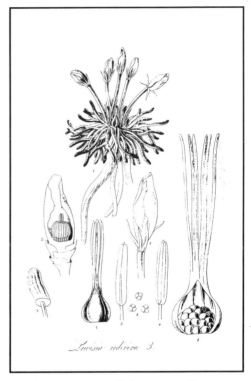

Thomas Drummond's bitterroot collection; from Hooker, 1830.

Frazer Tolmie in the northwest United States and in adjacent Canada. Tolmie collected in the late 1820s and his plants were not seen by Hooker until after 1830. The Tolmie plants, together with others collected in California by the Beechey Expedition, formed a complete set; some had flowers, some had only leaves and roots, and some had capsules. "Thus we are enabled," Hooker wrote, "to give a more complete account than has yet appeared of this plant, so well known to the Indians of N.W. America, and so much employed by them as an article of food".[43] These plants, however, could not be revived, so Hooker was again denied the pleasure of seeing living plants.

In 1863 Europe was made fully aware of both the beauty of bitterroot and its amazing power of revival. Hooker, by then Director of the Royal Gardens at Kew and the most influential and prestigious botanist of the times,[44] had received dried specimens destined for the Kew Herbarium. The bitterroot had been collected in southern British Columbia by Dr. David Lyall, R. N., surgeon and naturalist to the British Northwest Boundary Survey. Hooker plunged the dried plants in boiling water to prepare them for mounting and then stored them away. A year and a half later, noticing that the specimens still seemed to be alive, Hooker planted them. At least one bitterroot flourished and produced flowers at Kew in May of 1863,[45] surpassing all previous attempts and completely vindicating the name *rediviva*.

Following the custom of the times, Hooker then had produced a colored lithograph of the entire plant. This illustration of very high quality was accompanied by Latin and English descriptions and was published in Curtis's Botanical Magazine in 1863. This was apparently the first published illustration of a living and flowering bitterroot[46] though, by that time, it would surely have been seen, sketched and described by many western travelers. Hooker was very pleased, writing "we have at length the satisfaction of giving a figure, from a living plant, of *Lewisia rediviva . . .* of which hitherto little has been known."[49]

One of these travellers was the tireless Jesuit, Pierre-Jean DeSmet who, in 1846, commented on the abundance of the "bitter and camash roots"[47] in what is now eastern Washington. He must also have seen bitterroot in many other places and he certainly knew of its value. At about the same time, a fellow Jesuit, Gregory Mengarini, lay almost dead of hunger in the Bitterroot Valley. In a later account, he wrote that an old Indian woman had brought him some boiled bitterroot roots and insisted he eat them. "The roots were bitter", he wrote, "but I had to eat them. My vomiting, dizziness and lightness of head ceased, and soon I was well again".[48]

Hooker was modest and misleading. His own descriptions and sketches of 1830 and 1841 supplemented the earlier notes of Pursh in 1814 and of Thomas Nuttall in 1818. Nuttall followed up with another description in 1834 after examining Nathaniel Wyeth's collections. John Torrey and Asa Gray, America's leading botanists, also described bitterroot in *A Flora of North America* (dedicated to Hooker), published in 1838-1840.

LEWIS'S BITTERROOT COLLECTION

Between the publication of Pursh's *Flora* in 1814 and the successful cultivation and subsequent illustrated description of bitterroot by Hooker, no reference was made to Lewis's type collection of 1 July 1806. No botanist mentioned it, and its disposition was unknown. Thomas Nuttall, in *The Genera of North American Plants*, had no knowledge of it though he was aware, as was Hooker, of Pursh's description of Lewis's collection. Torrey and Gray mentioned the bitterroot collections of Lewis, Douglas, Drummond, Wyeth and Tolmie. Using a technique of the times, they placed an exclamation mark (!) after the collector's name if they had seen either his collection or another from the same locality.[50] In their description of bitterroot, only Lewis's name was not followed by this mark.

Bitterroot, first published illustration from a living plant; from Hooker, 1863.
(Note similarities with Hooker's 1830 illustration).

Where was Lewis's type collection throughout most of the nineteenth century? All that is known for certain is that it was in the hands of Bernard McMahon for a few years after 1807. McMahon wrote to Thomas Jefferson on 24 December 1809, "I have, I believe, all his [Lewis's] collection of dried specimens of plants, procured during his journey to the pacific ocean".[51] Actually, McMahon had only the plants collected on the return journey; material collected on the westbound trip (some of which was lost) was in the possession of Benjamin Smith Barton.

Barton had been the original choice to edit the botanical material of the expedition. Though an eminent botanist, he had a reputation as "a notoriously dilatory man." He invariably took on more than he could handle and his tendency to overestimate his output was well known to his contemporaries.[52] Barton had "varied interests" and an "enthusiastic temperament," wrote botanist Francis Pennell in 1950, "that led him to take up project after project only to abandon each in turn".[53] He was also in ill health and though expectations were kept up for some production on his part, he accomplished nothing with the Lewis and Clark plants. He died in 1815, leaving "an immense heap of papers, and in such disorder,"[54] and contributing a major share to the mystery of the lost Lewis and Clark plants.

The plants held by McMahon, including Lewis's bitterroot, were examined by Pursh between 1807 and 1810. William Clark wrote that he had paid Pursh (Clark refers to him as Purch, Perche and Perch but never as Pursh)[55] for his labors. He also wrote, in 1810, that he had found the "original specimens of these plants" but "I find some difficuelty of getting a proper scientifcul charrutor to compile that part of the work relitive to Botany, Mineralogy & Zoology, however I do not dispare".[56]

Barton emerged as the "proper scientifcul charrutor" and by 1810, it appears he had most of the Lewis and Clark botanical collections, including the type bitterroot. The remainder, some thirty-nine plants, were taken to London by Pursh and eventually returned to the United States. Both Clark and Nicholas Biddle, the original editor of the journals, realized that Barton had done nothing and, in 1816, Clark requested Biddle to deliver to Thomas Jefferson "the specimens which were in the possession of Doctor Barton".[57] Apparently this was done although as late as 1826, Clark intimated that some of the specimens may still have been held by Barton's estate.[58] Jefferson apparently deposited the plants with the American Philosophical Society, where he was a member, and there they lay, forgotten, until 1896. No one knew of their existence, not even the indefatigable Elliott Coues, who published his heavily annotated edition of the Lewis and Clark journals in 1893.

In 1896, Thomas Meehan, a botanist associated with the Academy of Natural Sciences, was encouraged by Charles Sprague Sargent[59] to search for the lost plants. After what Meehan described as a "long and diligent search" among stored items in custody of the American Philosophical Society, he found packages of plants that he correctly determined to be the Lewis and Clark collections. "With the freedom of three-quarters of a century the museum beetles had made sad work in the bundles" Meehan wrote, and a few specimens "had been wholly reduced to dust".[60] Nevertheless, the collection was in fair condition. One hundred eighty-four herbarium sheets were found, including the type collection of bitterroot.[61]

Meehan examined the collection and then referred it to Dr. Benjamin Lincoln Robinson of the Gray Herbarium at Harvard. Robinson and J. M. Greenman studied the plants and made all possible identifications. Their careful work remains authoritative. Meehan published the results in 1898 and the plants were deposited in the herbarium of the Academy of Natural Sciences of Philadelphia. The collection, including Lewis's bitterroot, is there today.

Elliott Coues followed up on Meehan's paper with one of his own entitled "Notes on Mr. Thomas Meehan's Paper on the Plants of Lewis and Clark's Expedition Across the Continent, 1804-06".[62] In it, Coues, not a botanist, had no argument with Meehan's botanical determinations. He wrote that he (Coues) "could give the precise locality of every specimen which bears a date in the herbarium that Mr. Meehan recently discovered", something Meehan had not done. Coues's locality for Lewis's bitterroot is close enough but not necessarily "precise." He fixed the site of the type collection "at the mouth of Traveller's Rest Creek [Lolo Creek] of L & C", and the plant is found today above the east bank of the Bitterroot River opposite the mouth of Lolo Creek. Coues concluded with a comment on the "geography that satisfies botanists," adding "nothing of the sort would satisfy a zoologist, I am sure".[63]

Meriwether Lewis's bitterroot collection was returned to Montana for a brief visit in 1929. In that year, Genevieve Murray completed a master's thesis at the University of Montana on the bitterroot. Her advisor, Arthur L. Stone, Dean of the School of Journalism, had guided Elliott Coues through the Bitterroot Valley in 1893.[64] Coues was tracing the route of the Lewis and Clark expedition, and it was on this trip that he determined the type location of the bitterroot collection.

Murray requested the loan of the type collection from the Academy of Natural Sciences of Philadelphia. The loan was granted by Dr. Francis Pennell of the Academy with apparently some influence being exerted by Morton J. Elrod of the University of Montana faculty. According to Murray,

The original bitterroot collection (six plants) of 1 July 1806. Only dried flowers and a few stems remain.

This label by Thomas Meehan in the 1890s.

This label in Pursh's handwriting. Part above line copied by Pursh from Lewis's original note accompanying collection. Part below line Pursh's comments on plant. Words "Lewis" and "Pursh" added by Meehan.

*Original herbarium sheet of Lewis's bitterroot collection,
Academy of Natural Sciences, Philadelphia (facsimile)*

Meehan's search in 1896 had <u>not</u> turned up the type bitterroot collection (though it was listed by him and was examined by Robinson and Greenman of the Gray Herbarium) and only another letter of inquiry from her resulted in finding the bitterroot.[65] After several exchanges of correspondence, the type bitterroot collection was mailed to Missoula in April of 1929 along with other unspecified bitterroot specimens from the academy. The Lewis bitterroots were photographed and their story written up in state newspapers.[66] Murray was thrilled by the loan from the Academy and concluded her thesis "The loan of the type specimen to the University of Montana in April, 1929, was unprecidented [sic], its reception ecstatic".[67]

ENDNOTES

1. Thwaites, 3, p. 13.

2. Coues, 2, p. 543-4. The identification was made by Frank H. Knowlton of the U.S. National Museum who did many of Coues's plant identifications without, however, seeing any plants. Coues was not a botanist.

3. Thwaites, 3, p. 13.

4. Changes in some Lewis and Clark place names are traced by Jackson, *Among the Sleeping Giants*. Lolo Creek, for example, was variously known as Traveller's Rest Creek, St. Regis de Borgia, Lou-Lou Creek and Lo Lo Fork. p. 19-20.

5. Determined by Coues in 1893. Five years later, he wrote, "if there is any thing I do know, it is exactly where Lewis and Clark were on every day, almost every hour, from start to finish of their famous expedition". Coues, Notes, p. 291.

6. Thwaites, 5, p. 181. The others were *Trifolium microcephalus* (clover), *Sedum stenopetalum* (stonecrop) and *Orthocarpus tenuifolius* (owl clover). Cutright, p. 24, p. 28, p. 38.

7. Coues, Notes, p. 292. Also, Piper, p. 11.

8. Cutright, p. 298.

9. Thwaites, 5, p. 95-97, "I met with a singular plant today in blume which I preserved a specemine . . . " [Lewis].

10. Thwaites, 5, p. 173, p. 182. Identification by C. V. Piper in 1893. Other identifications in Thwaites by Dr. William Trelease of The Missouri Botanical Garden.

11. The type collection is synonymous with the type specimen (the first verified collection of a new plant).

12. Thwaites, 5, p. 175 note. See also Space, p. 36; "The spring of 1806 must have been unusually late."

13. Cutright, p. 305. Cutright's reference is to the entire collection brought back by the expedition.

14. *The Missoulian*, May 5, 1929. In 1812 Frederick Pursh wrote that the petals of Lewis's bitterroot were "white, veined with rose" (*petala alba roseo-venosa*). "Society Papers" Collection, The Linnean Society.

15. Cutright, p. 305.

16. Leonard Wiley is one of the few modern authors who seem to be aware that Lewis collected only white-flowered bitterroot. "It was from the rare white form of *L. rediviva* in the expedition's herbarium collection that Pursh named the genus and the first species discovered." Wiley, p. 233.

17. Ronda says "Far too much has been made of Lewis's scientific abilities. Largely self-taught, he was a keen amateur naturalist but no match for his European contemporaries." Ronda, p. 7. Nevertheless, Lewis was "advised," as Moulton writes, by Benjamin Smith Barton and Caspar Wistar, the best America had to offer. Moulton, 2, p. 6 note.

18. McMahon's letter in Jackson, p. 398.

19. Pennell, p. 144 note.

20. Meehan, p. 19.

21. Cutright, p. viii.

22. Pursh, 2, p. 368. In an 1812 letter Pursh wrote that the roots were "taken out of the herbarium where they had been longer than a year, they vegetated & were kept growing for more than a twelvemonth then some unfortunate accident destroyed [?] them". "Society Papers" Collection, The Linnean Society.

23. Jackson, p. 399 note.

24. Cutright, p. 367.

25. Pursh, 1, p. vi.

26. Fernald, p. 66 note. Fernald adds that Pursh was a "hopeless drunkard". Ibid.

27. The others were *Clarkia* (ragged robin), *Calochortus* (mariposa), and *Tigarea* (antelope brush). *Tigarea* was later changed to *Purshia*. Pursh originally named another new genus after Lewis; his first notes on *Berberis aquifolium* labeled that plant *Lewisia aquifolium*. Pennell, p. 193.

28. Meehan, p. 19. In his 1812 letter Pursh wrote that Lewis had referred in his journal to bitterroot as "Red-root of the Missouri". This is puzzling as Lewis knew he was not on the Missouri when he collected bitterroot. Was there an earlier collection now lost? "Society Papers" Collection, The Linnean Society.

29. Pursh, 2, p. 368.

30. Cutright, p. 363. Fernald says the *Flora* was "amazingly brilliant". Fernald, p. 66.

31. Nuttall, 2, p. 13-14. Ewan says this is an example that "feelings were strained and embittered by competition" between Pursh and Nuttall. Ewan, p. 607.

32. Pursh first described the new genus *Lewisia* in a letter to Aylmour Lambert, 20 January 1812. "Society Papers" Collection, The Linnean Society.

33. Sir Aylmour Lambert, Pursh's English sponsor, was Vice President of the Linnean Society. He probably read the paper. Ibid. Also McKelvey, p. 77-8.

34. Jackson, p. 463 note.

35. McMahon to Jefferson, 17 January 1809, Jefferson Papers, Ser. II, v. 59, No. 63. True, p. 10

36.   Details in Ewan, p. 623.

37.   Presumably, he meant flowering plants. Hooker, 1830, p. 344.

38.   Hooker, 1830, p. 345. Saunders says bitterroot was "introduced into England in
        1826." This is probably a reference to Douglas's collection and the unsuccessful
        cultivation of it. Saunders, p. 27.

39.   Hooker, 1830, p. 345. But Drummond did not mention bitterroot in the account of
        his travels which was edited by Hooker in 1830.

40.   Pursh, 2, p. 368.

41.   Hooker and Walker-Arnott, p. 344.

42.   Hooker, 1830, p. 344-356.

43.   Hooker and Walker-Arnott, p. 344.

44.   We read of Hooker that "he always rose early, went little into society, and retired
        late" and that "he always completed the works that he planned," article by W. R.
        Morfill in *Dictionary of National Biography*. In 1871, C. C. Parry wrote that
        Hooker possessed "a most happy combination of rare personal attractions, together
        with a high order of executive ability, joined to untiring industry ...". Parry, p. 109.
        Parry had recently visited Hooker at Kew.

45.   Hooker, 1863, Tab. 5395. This is commented on by, among others. Elrod, n. p. and
        R. Brown, p. 85.

46.   Rudd, p. 354.

47.   DeSmet, p. 241.

48.   Mengarini, p.11.

49.   Hooker, 1863, Tab. 5395. The beautiful illustration was the work of W. Fitch, artist
        and lithographer, and printer Vincent Brooks.

50.   Torrey and Gray, 1, p. xiv.

51.   Letter in Jackson, p. 485.

52.   Jackson, p. 161 note.

53.   Pennell, p. 139.

54.   According to José Corréa de Serra, Jackson, p. 608 note.

55.   Pursh was born Friedrich Traugott Pursch (Ewan, p. 601) so Clark only established
        a few other variations of the original spelling. Pursh himself signed his name as
        Frederick Pursh.

56.   Letter, Clark to William D. Meriwether, January 26, 1810. Jackson, p. 490.

57.   Letter in Jackson, p. 623.

58.   Letter, Clark to Albert Gallatin. Jackson, p. 644.

59.   Sargent was an eminent silviculturist interested in, among many other subjects, the trees described by Lewis and Clark.

60.   Meehan, p. 14.

61.   Modern research by Cutright now places the number of herbarium species at 216. Cutright, p. 367.

62.   Coues, Notes, 1898.

63.   Coues, Notes, p. 291-93. Coues was, of course, a zoologist.

64.   Stone, p. 17.

65.   Murray, p. 16. The bitterroot probably had been misplaced again after Meehan originally found it in 1896.

66.   An example is the article "The Lewis Bitter Root Back Home," with photo. *The Missoulian*, May 5, 1929.

67.   Murray, p. 41.

3

CLASSIFICATION

Bitterroot was given the scientific name *Lewisia rediviva* Pursh in 1814 and so it has remained through the years. Not only was Pursh's the first description of a new species, but also it was the first description of the new genus *Lewisia*. Since that time, many other species have been assigned to *Lewisia*[1] and all of these species have, at one time or another, been reclassified and renamed. Within the genus, only bitterroot has passed unscathed through the trials of nomenclatural change.

Frederick Pursh listed bitterroot under class Polyandria, order Monogynia[2] (now discarded nomenclature), and soon after, *Lewisia* was classified within the family Portulacaceae where it remains today. According to Mathew, there has never been any real doubt that *Lewisia* belongs in the family Portulacaceae A. L. de Jussieu (1789)[3], but there have been lapses. In 1889, for example, a British text, after mentioning the three common names of *Lewisia rediviva* (bitterroot, *racine amere,* and *spatlum*), stated that *Lewisia rediviva* "is the only species of this singular genus of the *Mesembryaceae*".[4] As long ago as 1834, Thomas Nuttall wrote that bitterroot was "apparently almost intermediate between *Ficoideae* and *Cacteae* . . . but much nearer to the latter".[5] Modern taxonomists give some consideration to the familial similarities of Portulacaceae and Cactaceae[6] and there is no question that bitterroot flowers and some cactus flowers,

Cushion cactus (Coryphantha vivipara). *Thomas Nuttall believed that bitterroot and cactus were closely related.*

particularly those of cushion cactus (*Coryphantha vivipara*) are remarkably similar in appearance. Nuttall also believed that "this very curious and showy plant [bitterroot] constitutes a very distinct natural order." He published the order name Spaetalumeae[7] following the vernacular for the plant. This commendable recognition of the native name met with opposition from Hooker and Walker-Arnott who felt it "barbarous" to commemorate the Indian name *spatlum*. They further believed it was unnecessary to construct a new order but if it were, they wrote, "surely the name *Lewisieae* is much to be preferred".[8] Hooker and Walker-Arnott had hesitated because Torrey and Gray in their *Flora* had limited the order Portulaceae to those genera with two or three sepals.[9] Nuttall's Spaetalumeae never did attract support, but it should be pointed out that most taxonomists today believe that bitterroot is a very distinct species with few close allies.[10] These allies, *Lewisia maguirei* and *L. disepala*, were unknown to science in Nuttall's time so his determination was definitely valid.

Though the Latin binomial name of bitterroot has never changed, the plant has been known by many common names. Bitterroot is by far the most popular, as well as the most descriptive name, though a modern author considers it "perhaps a rather dull name for such an attractive species".[11] Hooker in 1863 listed "spat'lum" and "reviving Lewisia" as common names.[12] In 1905, J. W. Blankinship and Hester F. Henshall added "red-head Louisa" and the already well-known "*racine amere*" to the published list.[13] Red-head Louisa should be rejected outright for obvious reasons, but *racine amere* should be retained for its accuracy and historical significance. A form of *racine amere* first appeared in print in 1823 when Alexander Ross wrote "we raised camp and proceeded on our journey up what is called the Valley of Racine aux Mere, or Spetlum country".[14] Spurious names that have appeared over the years include "sand rose", "wild portulaca", "mountain rose",[15] "rock rose" and "resurrection flower".[16] All of these should be dropped though undoubtedly some or all will persist in certain areas.

A very puzzling reference is found in a letter, dated 20 January 1812, from Frederick Pursh to Aylmour Lambert. In this, the first (though unpublished) description of *Lewisia rediviva*, Pursh wrote that the plant "is found on the banks of the upper part of the Missouri & called by Governor Lewis in his journal Red-root of the Missouri".[17] Lewis certainly knew that his collection of 1 July 1806 was not on the Missouri or even east of the Continental Divide. Either Pursh described a bitterroot specimen collected earlier and then lost, or the "Red-root of the Missouri" refers to the roots confiscated by Drouillard on 22 August 1805. There is no mention in Lewis's journal of "Red-root of the Missouri" nor did Pursh use this name in his *Flora Americae Septentrionalis* of 1814.

The species *Lewisia rediviva* has been the subject of very little taxonomic splitting. Hooker, in his *Flora Boreali-Americana* of 1840, listed two

*Pursh's unpublished mention of Lewis's
"red root of the Missouri", 1812.*

forms of bitterroot: the alpha form from Pursh with "*radice sanguineo, flore albo*" (blood-colored root, white flower) and the beta form, "*radice albo, flore roseo*" (white root, rose flower), of Drummond's collection. The beta form was rejected when Hooker discovered that the white root was white because it had been peeled for use as food.[18]

A white-flowered form of bitterroot was described and published as *Lewisia alba* Kellogg in 1861. It is now listed only as a synonym[19] and has no significance as a taxonomic entity. Per Axel Rydberg, in 1932, described *Lewisia minor* Rydberg but later this was changed to *Lewisia rediviva* variety *minor* (Rydberg) Munz.[20] In the most recent taxonomic alteration, variety *minor* has become *Lewisia rediviva* subspecies *minor* (Rydberg) Holmgren.[21] As the name implies, it differs from the common form in the size of flowers. Subspecies *minor* and subspecies *rediviva* are currently the only two recognized taxa within the species.[22] A variety, *Lewisia rediviva* "Winifred Herdman," was once in cultivation in England. It is described as "having large flowers of an almost purple hue". Originally collected in the Okanagon Valley of British Columbia, it now seems to be unknown both in cultivation and in the wild.[23] Another variety, *Lewisia rediviva* "Jolon", is also large-flowered (up to three inches in diameter) and is still in cultivation. However, its color does not come true,[24] so its exact status is questionable.

As a genus of plants, *Lewisia* has certain similarities to other genera, and these similarities have brought forth various taxonomic interpretations by different authors. In 1818, Nuttall wrote that bitterroot, which he had not yet seen, was closely related to the genus *Sempervivum* "and appertaining to the

Lewisia rediviva *variety* minor, *Nye County, Nevada, 7,800 feet.*

same natural order".[25] Nuttall's ideas on the relationships of *Lewisia* are always interesting, but the *Lewisia/Sempervivum* concept appears invalid. In the most recent taxonomic treatment of the genus, *Lewisia* is considered to be strictly a North American genus. Its nearest relative, *Calandrinia*, once regarded as congeneric by some authors, extends no farther north than Mexico.[26]

Apart from bitterroot, other members of the genus (as now recognized by the majority of authors) have been assigned at times to the genera *Erocallis* and *Oreobrama*. William A. Weber of Colorado has revived these distinctions, separating *Erocallis* from *Lewisia* and *Oreobrama* on the basis of its round corm as opposed to the taproot of the other two genera. *Oreobrama* is separated from *Lewisia* on the bases of smaller flowers, lack of jointed pedicel and by the leaves appearing with the flowers.[27] Weber's "splitter" approach has much to recommend it, but other modern treatments do not accept his division of the genus *Lewisia*. The usual classification is to lump all *Lewisia*, *Erocallis* and *Oreobrama* under *Lewisia*.[28]

On 27 June 1806, four days before the collection of the type specimen of bitterroot, Lewis and Clark collected an unknown plant "on the waters of the Kooskooskee [the Clearwater River in eastern Idaho] within the Rocky Mountains".[29] The plant was not mentioned in the journals and presumably was not examined until 1897 when Robinson and Greenman studied the collection discovered by Meehan. They named the plant *Lewisia triphylla* Robinson, aware that Sereno Watson had named a specimen of the same species *Claytonia triphylla* Watson in 1875.[30] Watson's was the first published description of the species, and his collection stands as the type collection. If Pursh had examined, described and published Lewis's 27 June 1806 specimen, it would have been the type collection, preceding Watson's by many years. It is interesting to speculate that if Pursh had studied the 27 June and 1 July 1806 collections together, he may have recognized the generic similarities. Conceivably then, the *Lewisia triphylla* of 27 June 1806 could have been the type, not only of the species, but also of the genus.

A new species, closely resembling bitterroot, was discovered in the mountains of south-central Nevada in 1945. The co-discoverers, Dr. Bassett Maguire and Dr. Arthur H. Holmgren, named it *Lewisia maguirei* Holmgren. Nine years later, Holmgren published the subgenus name *Eulewisia* to provide a taxonomic niche for *Lewisia maguirei*, *L. rediviva* and *L. disepala*.[31] This division has been maintained and, in 1966, R. C. Elliott published a monograph on lewisias that included a key to "groups" of species. His "rediviva group" is identical to Holmgren's subgenus *Eulewisia*. Thirteen other species of *Lewisia* were relegated to two other groups, the "cotyledon group" and the "pygmaea group".[32] A technical study led to further divisions and the addition of two new species of *Lewisia*, bringing the total number of species, in 1975, to eighteen.[33]

The latest classification of the genus and one that is, hopefully, the final word on the subject, is the recent monographic study by Brian Mathew. Published in 1989, *The Genus Lewisia* designates two subgenera with a total of nineteen species.[34] Subgenus *Lewisia* is broken down into six sections and subgenus *Strophiolum* contains only *Lewisia tweedyi*. One of Mathew's sections within subgenus *Lewisia*, also named *Lewisia*, contains *Lewisia rediviva*, *L. maguirei* and *L. disepala*. It is separated from other sections on the bases of the number, texture and color of the sepals and the disarticulate pedicel.[35] Currently, from family down to subspecies, the classification of *Lewisia rediviva* and near relatives is:

> Family: Portulacaceae
> Genus: *Lewisia*
> Subgenus: *Lewisia*
> Section: *Lewisia*
> 1: *Lewisia rediviva* Pursh (Red-root of the Missouri [?], bitterroot, *spatlum*, *racine amere*, reviving lewisia).
> -- subspecies *rediviva*
> -- subspecies *minor* (Rydberg) Holmgren
> 2: *Lewisia maguirei* Holmgren
> 3: *Lewisia disepala* Rydberg

Lewisia maguirei, *Nye County, Nevada, 7,700 feet.*

Lewisia disepala, *Yosemite National Park.*

ENDNOTES

1. According to Mathew, there are now (1989) nineteen species in the genus. Mathew, p. 42-44.

2. Pursh, II, p. 368. Bitterroot is now classified within class Magnoliopsida, subclass Caryophyllidae, order Caryophyllales. Cronquist, p. xiii-xiv.

3. Mathew, p. 11. Mathew also writes that Hooker and Walker-Arnott, in 1839, published the family name Lewisiaceae, but I find no mention of this. Ibid.

4. Lindley and Moore, II, p. 678. *Mesembryaceae* (or *Mesembryanthemaceae*) is now known as *Aizoaceae*, a family mostly made up of low succulent tropical and subtropical herbs and subshrubs.

5. Nuttall, 1834, p. 25.

6. Mathew, p. 11.

7. Nuttall, 1834, p. 23-25.

8. Hooker and Walker-Arnott, p. 345. Hooker's order #37 was Portulaceae in his *Flora Boreali-Americana*, I, p. 222.

9. Torrey and Gray, 1, p. 677.

10. Elliott, p. 5.

11. Mathew, p. 45.

12. Hooker, 1863, Tab. 5395.

13. Blankinship and Henshall, p. 135.

14. Ross, p. 213. The reference is to the Bitterroot Valley.

15. *Rocky Mountain Magazine*, 1902, p. 139, MHS File.

16. Mentioned but rejected by Daubenmire, p. 10.

17. Pursh to Lambert, 20 January 1812. "Society Papers" collection, The Linnean Society of London.

18. Hooker, 1840, I, p. 223.

19. Hitchcock and Cronquist, 2, p. 235.

20. Munz, p. 298.

21. Holmgren, p. 136; Mathew, p. 51.

22. According to Mathew, Ibid.

23. Elliott, p. 55. See also Heath, p. 339.

24. Mathew, p. 49.

25. Nuttall, 1818, 2, p. 13-14.

26. The differences between the two genera are based on capsule and pollen characters. Mathew, p. 11-12.

27. Thomas Howell first described *Oreobrama* in 1893. P. A. Rydberg first described *Erocallis* in 1906. W. Weber, p. 413-14.

28. For example, Hitchcock and Cronquist, *Flora*, p. 106 and Mathew, p. 13.

29. Lewis's herbarium label. Meehan, p. 19.

30. Watson, p. 345 and Piper, p. 246-47.

31. Holmgren, p. 135-37.

32. Elliott, p. 3-5.

33. Hohn, p. 4-5.

34. The nineteen species as listed by Mathew: *Lewisia rediviva, L. maguirei, L. disepala, L. kelloggii, L. brachycalyx, L. triphylla, L. oppositifolia, L. nevadensis, L. longipetala, L. sierrae, L. pygmaea, L. stebbinsii, L. congdonii, L. columbiana, L. leeana, L. cantelovii, L. serrata, L. cotyledon, L. tweedyi.* Mathew, p. 6.

35. Mathew, p. 40-43.

4
THE PLANT

HABITAT

Throughout its range, bitterroot is found on well-drained exposed sites in gravelly to heavy soils. Low spots, shady spots and places where water tends to accumulate and pool are avoided. In the Bitterroot Valley south of Missoula, bitterroot populations typically occur in deep, well-drained alluvium that has developed over clayey lake sediments. In the rooting zone a few inches below the surface, the soil is chiefly gravel and sand[1] with very little obvious loam. This does not seem to hold true everywhere and an observer in Wyoming notes that bitterroot there prefers "uniform silty loam with an increment of volcanic ash and usually free from gravel; sand, shales, and low spots are passed over".[2] In recently-discovered populations in the Blacktail Hills of Glacier National Park, the "soil" is finely fragmented and sedimentary in origin. Little sand or loam is evident and the growing medium appears to consist almost entirely of small diameter scree. Farther north in southwest Alberta, recent bitterroot finds grow in blowout areas on exposed ridges — spots where the prevailing strong winds and exposure have caused the removal of sod — and where the soils (lithosols) are derived from the outcropping bedrock.[3] There is speculation that bitterroot in some locations favors soils that are at least partially of volcanic origin.[4] In eastern Washington, bitterroot most frequently is found on basaltic outcroppings

Isolated bitterroot location, Glacier National Park, Montana.
Plants near crest of hill only.

Bitterroot in scree, Glacier National Park, Montana.

(but that may be because much of eastern Washington is underlain by basalt) where it usually occupies rocky crevices. This seeming partiality to basalt is also evident in the upper Yellowstone Valley of Montana and Wyoming.

Many gardeners know that soil composition is not a controlling factor in the cultivation of bitterroot. It is grown successfully in fertile garden soils and even in fertilized plots where watering is regular,[5] as well as in gritty sparse soils under arid conditions. The primary requirement is that the soil, whatever its composition, must drain (aerate)[6] well during the growing season. Winter wetness of soil can be tolerated, as in eastern Washington where bitterroot survives on flat basalt outcrops "where drainage is extremely poor and the soil remains completely saturated for weeks at a time".[7] Cultivators of native plants often learn more than do botanists about the requirements of their subjects. Gardeners in Great Britain have raised bitterroot for more than a century. A leading English plantsman writes that the genus *Lewisia* is "for the most part easy, they only require care in watering". Bitterroot, he continues, needs "plenty of water . . . when growth commences . . . but must be completely withheld once the plant dies down. All available sun baking is required".[8] To summarize the basic requirements of bitterroot: an open, well-drained growing medium, good exposure to sun and a minimum of moisture during the summer season. The last requirement is not absolute, because some populations, such as those in the upper Yellowstone Valley, receive heavy rainfall in May and June. Some growers also water regularly until the plant dies down.

SEASON OF GROWTH

Though most plants of temperate North America become dormant in fall and resume growth in spring,[9] bitterroot plants break dormancy in fall. The onset of cool weather, usually accompanied by rain, signals the beginning of new growth. In the Bitterroot Valley, this occurs in October and is marked by the appearance of tiny green leaves.[10] Below the surface, the buds that will become the flowers of the next summer begin to form, but they do not emerge until the following year. In higher and more northern locations, there may be no leaf emergence until the spring, but some subsurface growth occurs in late fall. Experiments indicate that low temperature is the critical factor in breaking dormancy. Even without rain, growth commences when temperature does not exceed 68°F for an undetermined period exceeding forty-eight hours. The conclusion of these experiments was that "photoperiodism [length of day] does not seem to be involved, but thermoperiodism [length of warmth] may be".[11] In southwest Alberta (and probably elsewhere), newly emerged leaves of garden plants seem impervious to extreme weather and are able to withstand at least -22°F with no snow cover.

Two well-known "herbarium" stories, however, indicate that dormant bitterroot plants may respond to neither moisture nor lowered temperature. In a Montana account, collected plants were potted in sand in the laboratory. The plants flowered and withered away and the pots were then set aside in a warm and dry room. "A year later, they were discovered growing vigorously, as if in their native sod." They had "received no water or other attention".[12] A better known story is Hooker's experience with Lyall's collection of 1861. Lyall had collected flowering plants in May or June of 1861. The plants, by then dried and presumably dead, were delivered to Hooker at Kew in early 1862. Hooker immersed them in boiling water "on account of its well-known tenacity of life" [he wished to prevent the dried plants from reviving!], then stored them away. Later, Hooker noticed that the plants showed signs of life. He planted them and in May of 1863, almost two years after Lyall had collected them in British Columbia, Hooker wrote, "they produced beautiful flowers in great perfection".[13]

Of twenty-seven collections of *Lewisia rediviva* in the herbarium of the University of Montana, six show that there had been definite sprouting of leaves after collection and drying. Three other specimens may have sprouted, though condition of these collections is so poor (one goes back to 1886), that it is impossible to say for sure.[14]

A flowering collection from northern Flathead County in Montana was dried and stored immediately after collection on 5 July 1990. In September of 1990, sprouts appeared. When taken from the herbarium and planted in June of 1991, a sprouted plant failed to revive. Possibly the plant would have continued to revive if it were planted immediately after sprouting.

These apparent inconsistencies have been explained in a recent technical study which states that internal controls protect bitterroot from breaking dormancy prematurely. This "internally-controlled dormancy process" insures against summer growth after flowering and is characteristic of bitterroot populations throughout the range of the species. The innate dormant period lasts for at least thirty days after flowering in the Bitterroot Valley[15] and may be shorter in populations that bloom later than the typical June flowering of southwest Montana. Dry and warm conditions, such as in herbaria, apparently prolong this dormant period. In some cases, dormancy has persisted through two and possibly more growing seasons. In nature, parallel instances of plants living through several years of drought illustrate this prolongation of dormancy when external stimuli are absent.

Sooner or later, internal controls lapse and environmental conditions dictate plant development. In Montana, and probably in other higher and colder parts of its range, bitterroot renews leaf growth in March. Days are then appreciably longer, moisture is available either from melting snow or spring rains and warm temperatures prevail. The long period of chilling -- from October to March in most populations -- is a requirement to continued floral development and without it, summer dormancy would not occur.[16] New leaves are added through April and at lower elevations, apical buds appear in early May. At Pullman, Washington, flowers began to open between 19 and 33 days after the appearance of buds.[17] In northern Montana

Bitterroot leaves in March, Southwest Alberta.

and southwest Alberta, these events occur about a month later; buds appear in June and early July is the blooming season. Fruit and seed are produced proportionately later.

Soon after the spring appearance of buds, the leaves began to turn red at their tips and shrink in length. These are the first signs of dormancy. The flowering season follows and by the time of full bloom, the leaves are in most cases completely withered away. Occasionally, short stubs of leaves persist after the appearance of flowers although they are obviously dead. The period of actual growth extends from the average first date of frost in the fall to the average last date of frost in the spring. Summed up, the "growing season is entirely contained within the frost season".[18] Though this conclusion is apt, it is not entirely applicable to bitterroot in higher and colder parts of its range. At higher latitudes and higher elevations, such as in northern Montana and southwest Alberta, frost occurs in all but two or three months. In rare years, frost occurs every month. It should be noted that flowering and development of seed are considered ripening rather than growing.

The flowering of bitterroot is, of course, the most remarkable event in the life history of this unusual plant. Modest descriptions refer to the flowers as large and showy. Somewhat more enthusiastic is the reference to the "quite astounding spectacle"[19] of the sudden appearance of blooms in the arid Pacific Northwest. An English botanist writes that bitterroot "is perhaps the most beautiful of all the lewisias with its huge soft satiny pink or white flowers which look extremely like cactus flowers in their petal texture and clarity of color".[20] This description is very similar to Thomas Nuttall's of 1834, "The flowers very large," Nuttall wrote, "wholly like that of a *Cactus*, rose red".[21]

THE FLOWER

The color of bitterroot flowers ranges from the deepest rose-red to pure white. Very few have been seen bearing flowers that only can be described as purple. These seem to be extremely rare. Most white-flowered examples have some tinge of rose in the petals, stamens or pistil. A few, however, are pure white throughout. One exceptional color phase was first described in 1871 by Sereno Watson. His tantalizingly brief note -- "Plant sometimes green with white flowers, but more often purplish"[22] -- resulted from collections made during the geological exploration of the fortieth parallel in 1867-1869. Currently, the only known natural occurrence of this color phase, also known as "Watson's phase", is near Stevensville, Montana.

At the Stevensville location, only three or four of "Watson's phase" were found among a large population of white- to rose-flowered bitterroot.[23]

Locally, the phase is known as "yellow bitterroot". Its most distinctive and different feature is the green (or yellow-green) of the stem, calyx and bracts as contrasted to the rose-purple-buff of these parts in typical bitterroot. Some individuals are faintly yellow at the base of the petals (but very faint) and the stamens are white or yellow rather than pink. The pistil is occasionally pure white. There is some merit to the "yellow" designation as there is a distinct, though often slight, yellow tinge to all parts in <u>some</u> plants. Thus far, it has not been determined if the "yellow" phase comes true from seed as the rose and white phases do.[24]

RIPENING

Bitterroot flowers are often two inches in diameter while the largest may reach three inches. The flowers apparently are pollinated by bees (and perhaps other insects) and since there is little if any odor and no nectar, the bees must be attracted by the color of the blooms.[25] Floral abortion may occur if cool rainy weather persists when the flowers are beginning to unfold.[26] Continued cold wet conditions discourage insect activity resulting in little or no pollination, hence reduced production of seed. Sunshine is not required for floral development, but heat is necessary (perhaps only 50°F) for expansion of flowers.

Pollination to seed dispersal is a brief period in the life history of a bitterroot plant. The development and ripening of seed occupies two to three weeks; shortly after[27] the structure containing the seeds (the disseminule) breaks away from the stem. The rooted plant is then totally subterranean; there are no attached parts above ground.

The disseminule, capped by the calyptra,[28] is well adapted to aid in dispersal of seeds. The petals and stamens twist around the developing seeds and, together with the sepals, dry to a papery consistency and texture. The stem bearing the disseminule breaks and the slightest breeze tumbles the flimsy structure containing the seeds against the nearest obstruction. The cap of dry petals and stamens (the calyptra) falls away and the seeds, up to 60 or 70 per flower, but usually much less, either separate immediately from the calyx or remain lodged in a receptacle within it for a brief, though undetermined, time.

Laboratory experiments indicate that 5% of seeds will germinate without stratification. The percentage of germinating seeds increases with the number of days the seeds are exposed to temperatures slightly above freezing. The effective cooling period probably does not exceed ninety days and maximum cooling benefits may result in 100% germination.[29] Under ideal conditions, both naturally and in gardens, germination rates result in

Disseminule (seeds in expanded calyx).
Calyptra (twisted petals and stamens) on left.

population renewal or increase under all conditions save destruction of habitat.

REVIVING

The roots of bitterroot are usually considered the reviving parts of the plant.[30] This is true only if the caudex is included. An experiment in 1991 demonstrated that roots can be removed from plants in May (in an attempt to simulate the gathering technique of Indians) and the rootless plants will flower and develop roots.[31] Most roots produce one rosette, but under certain conditions buds develop from lateral roots and produce multiple caudices. Each caudex can, in turn, produce a rosette, but this sequence of events apparently is uncommon.[32] In the Blacktail Hills population of Montana, however, multiple caudices and rosettes from single roots are common. The production of more than the usual solitary caudex and root is probably a result of rapid growth in an abrasive medium. It also could be caused by external stimuli such as frost heaving, disturbance by animals or harvesting by humans.

DISTRIBUTION

In 1975, Rexford Daubenmire published a map illustrating the distribution of bitterroot throughout its natural range. Montana, Washington, Idaho and Oregon lead in abundance, California and Wyoming follow, respectively. Widely scattered populations occur in Colorado, Utah, Nevada and

Bitterroot with multiple caudices and rosettes, Glacier National Park, Montana.

Arizona. No bitterroot is found in the wet coastal parts of California, Oregon and Washington.[33] Kirkwood, among others, speculated that bitterroot spread from a center of origin in the Sierra Nevada of California.[34] If this is the case, the present distribution pattern suggests that the scattered populations of Arizona, Utah, Colorado and Nevada represent range retraction from those areas.[35] At the same time, bitterroot may be spreading to the north under continuing warmer and dryer climatic influences.

In its range, bitterroot is found at all but the lowest elevations, and is typically a plant of montane valleys, slopes, and ridges. A record for both highest elevation and latest blooming date may be that from 9,800 feet on Mt. Grant in Mineral County, Nevada, on July 28.[36]

Bitterroot favors areas that tend to be relatively dry in the summer and wet or snow covered in the winter. Exceptions occur and, in places where spring and summer rains are common, bitterroot grows on steep slopes where drainage is very rapid. Northern Montana populations on both sides of the continental divide survive only because the occasionally frequent and heavy rains of summer are immediately drained away from the plants. Rapid draining, in other words, is a substitute for the summer desiccation that characterizes other bitterroot areas such as the Bitterroot Valley. The annual amount of rainfall is not critical since bitterroot grows in areas that receive as much as 40 inches or as little as 6 inches per year.[37]

Neither is winter temperature a limiting factor. In parts of its range, low temperature in winter reaches -40°F. In other locations, for example southern California, freezing temperatures are seldom reached. High summer temperatures prevail throughout the range of bitterroot.

Since Daubenmire's study, the known range of bitterroot has been extended to the north. In the summer of 1982, bitterroot was found in southwest Alberta 13 miles west of Pincher Creek and about 48 miles east of the nearest population. This was a first record for Alberta[38] though a dubious newspaper story of 1951 reported that bitterroot "shies from civilization and is to be found in a few mountain valleys of Montana and Alberta."[39] In 1989, two populations were found one mile and closer west of the continental divide in northern Flathead County, Montana. At the time, the closest known population of bitterroot was near Bigfork, Montana, approximately 40 miles to the west. In 1990-1991, three separate bitterroot populations were located in northern Glacier County, Montana, in and near Glacier National Park. One of these was only a few miles from the Flathead County location.

DISPERSAL

The earliest explanation on the origin of the Alberta discovery suggested recent wind dispersal from the west. The source was believed to be the bitterroot populations in southeast British Columbia.[40] In 1988, a paper published in the same journal stated that "the wind-dispersal hypothesis should be used with caution". Two alternate theories were discussed: cultural dispersal and natural dispersal by past range expansion.[41]

Bitterroot seems admirably adapted for wind dispersal. Though the disseminule containing the seeds is over an inch in diameter, it weighs only 1/10 of a gram.[42] The slightest breeze at ground level sets the papery seed carriers rolling and tumbling, but it is doubtful if anything but hurricane-like winds could carry the disseminules over miles of forested terrain. Claude Barr, an authority on vegetation of the Great Plains, is a firm advocate of wind dispersal. "Some day," he writes, "a whirling air current will waft a cargo of [bitterroot] seed across the narrow Belle Fourche River, and the final 45 miles of Wyoming will have been entered". Barr refers to the disseminule as a "chambered nautilus" and writes that it "has happily taken advantage of the urgent winds and voyaged eastward".[43]

Perhaps wind dispersal can effect short distance range extensions, but in the case of the northern Flathead County populations, it is inconceivable that seeds could have been airborne over miles of wooded country. On the other hand, the population in Glacier County within Glacier National Park

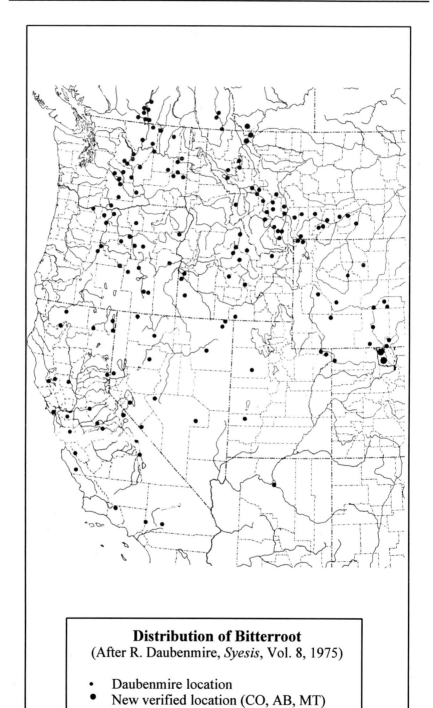

Distribution of Bitterroot
(After R. Daubenmire, *Syesis*, Vol. 8, 1975)

- Daubenmire location
- New verified location (CO, AB, MT)

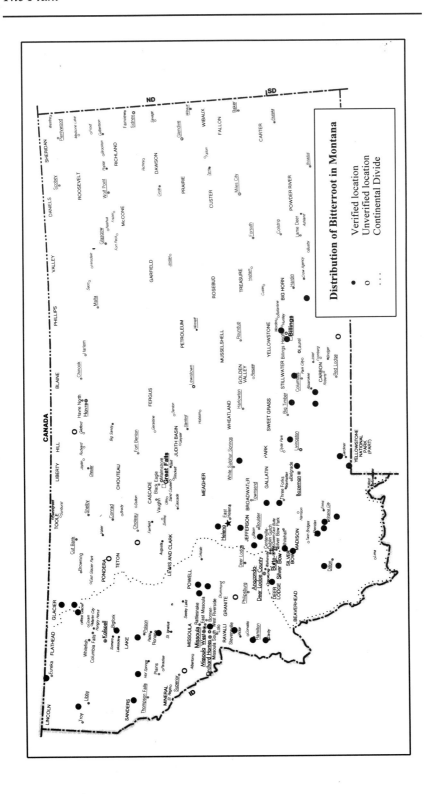

could have originated by wind dispersal from the northern Flathead County sites. It is downwind only a few miles and in the path of persistent and strong southwesterly winds.

Cultural dispersal of bitterroot only recently has attracted support from academicians. However, there seems to be a legend of origin among the Upper Kutenai that traces both bitterroot and blue camas to the discarding of roots from far away.[44] The discarded roots subsequently grew and bitterroot and blue camas both spread where the two plants had not grown before. Among the Flathead, there is some knowledge of unsuccessful attempts at planting bitterroot.[45] Intentional attempts to grow bitterroot by Indians (if it ever did occur) may have been suggested and encouraged by Jesuits, particularly Pierre-Jean DeSmet, in the middle nineteenth century.[46] Whatever the case, no known records exist concerning such a practice. The Indians of the area of Montana in particular were hunters and gatherers with little awareness of plant cultivation. One notable exception is the mysterious cultivation of tobacco by the Upper Kutenai, or by their predecessors, near the site of Eureka, Montana.[47]

Active cultural dispersal (planting seeds or roots) or passive cultural dispersal (accidental dropping of seeds or other plant parts) of bitterroot is a topic of continuing interest. Regarding the Alberta populations, the advocates of cultural dispersal write:

> Localized, disjunct occurrences of plants that were economically important [to] native groups therefore cannot be assessed fully without consideration of the possibility of cultural dispersal. Adventitious plantings of such species [including bitterroot] beyond their normal range would make economic sense in providing local supplies to supplement or even supplant long-distance trade, and to provide "wayside stops" along seasonal migration routes. Native use and trade would also have resulted in occasional accidental plantings.[48]

Botanists usually take a dim view of this subject and rely instead upon the traditionally accepted methods of dispersal:[49] geological events, wind, birds, etc.

The theory of cultural dispersal also can be applied to the recent finds of bitterroot in Flathead and Glacier counties. At the Flathead County site, little imagination is required to visualize eastbound Flathead or Kutenai Indians stopping on their way over Marias Pass. All the needs for camping -- wood, water, grass and game -- are present and have been present for thousands of years. This pass would be the last stop before crossing the divide and entering the territory of the hostile Blackfeet. Many other species of edible plants grow there. To complete the imaginary picture, Indians carrying bitterroot would have stopped and roots with regenerative parts or seeds would have been dropped accidentally or planted. Plant growth and spread would then follow and the bitterroot would persist after the introduction into what was probably a reasonably stable plant community. The concept seems far-fetched, but not impossible.

At two of the Glacier County sites, another aspect of cultural influence is involved. At one, bitterroot grows on a ridgetop that was once a burial place. This ridge is still visited by Blackfeet and continues to have religious significance. Another bitterroot location is near a modern vision site; whether it was also an ancient religious site is unknown.

The presence of isolated populations of bitterroot at religious sites may be more than coincidental. Early Native Americans could have brought bitterroot to these sites to enhance their cultural significance. Another possibility is that the sites could have been chosen because of the presence of bitterroot.[50]

The third Glacier County site is close to the mountains and, as far as is known, without traditional or modern religious significance. Fewer than 30 plants were counted in July of 1991 and the site can be considered impoverished.

One author of the 1988 paper on the Alberta find prefers what he calls "altithermal natural dispersal". In this opinion, the bitterroot are a "relict occurrence of a formerly widespread species". At two intervals between 9000 and 3000 years ago, warmer and drier conditions than those at present prevailed in southwest Alberta.[51] A different flora existed that was more suited to this climate. Bitterroot is one of many species that were more widespread and that have since undergone range retraction. It is, therefore, a relic of the past, persisting only in localized, highly specific sites.

Besides wind dispersal, cultural dispersal and altithermal natural dispersal, another means, bird dispersal, has been briefly mentioned to explain the Alberta bitterroot.[52] This has been a popular way to explain scattered and puzzling plant distributions for many years. It never can be proven that it does not happen, and certainly it does happen on a limited scale, but if dispersal of bitterroot seeds by birds were only moderately effective, it seems that populations would be much less scattered than they are now.

Recent geological studies in the vicinity of Marias Pass and elsewhere support the view of natural dispersal of bitterroot at least in northern Montana sites. Based on the dating of recent geological events by the discovery and known deposit date of two volcanic ash falls, these studies state that deglaciation of the Marias Pass area occurred before 11,400 years ago. During the time of the ash falls (11,200 years ago and circa 11,400 years ago), local vegetation in the area consisted of shrubs, herbs and scattered conifers -- "these vegetation data are characteristic of the tundra/subalpine forest boundary (treeline)". At that time, tree line was about 500 meters lower than the Marias Pass bitterroot sites.[53] This open landscape would have been more favorable than the present one for the occurrence of bitterroot.

Warm and dry climate prevailed about 9000 to 5000 years ago and again between 4000 and 3000 years ago.[54] These conditions conceivably could have contributed to the persistence of established bitterroot or allowed for the range expansion of the species from nearby western populations.

The area covered by the northern Montana bitterroot populations was glaciated and deglaciated during the same stages and intervals.[55] Theoretically, then, the entire area would have been revegetated with the same flora after the recession of the last glaciers more than 11,400 years ago. The two warm and dry intervals also would have contributed to a similar flora throughout the area. Only the climatic events in the last few thousands of years have caused the development of a diverse flora from Marias Pass to the western limits of the prairie grasslands.

The most reasonable theory to explain the northern Montana and southwest Alberta sites seems to be a modification of the "altithermal natural dispersal" explanation. At the disappearance of the montane and piedmont glaciers over 11,400 years ago, the deglaciated terrain was revegetated by plants, including bitterroot, characteristic of a warmer and drier climate than the prevailing regime. The source of the bitterroot was to the west. Other plants may have migrated from the plains or the mountains. The two warmer intervals between 9000 and 3000 years ago contributed to this xeric (dry land) flora. Exposed slopes and ridge tops still support bitterroot in very restricted locations near Marias Pass and in southwest Alberta. These sites are surrounded by variable terrain and, particularly to the west, the vegetative cover is unsuitable to the growth of bitterroot. Nearby bitterroot locations in Glacier County could have originated in the same way or they could be products of wind dispersal from the Marias Pass sites.

COLOR VARIATION

Across its range, bitterroot populations display a wide range of color. In the Sierra Nevada of California, bitterroot has "much the look" of typical

COLOR VARIATIONS

Lewisia rediviva *subspecies* rediviva

Rose red, Glacier National Park, Montana.

Typical pink, Flathead National Forest, Montana.

White, Stevensville, Montana.

"Watson's phase", Stevensville, Montana.

White on lava, Craters of the Moon National Monument, Idaho.

Red-purple, Hamilton, Montana.

Montana bitterroot "except for being paler, whitish or ivory to pinkish."[56] Toward the Rocky Mountains, the flowers of bitterroot seem to be progressively redder or more deeply pink. In the interior valleys, however, and particularly in the Bitterroot Valley of Montana,[57] there is much color variation. Pure white flowers are not rare at lower elevations though Wiley, when he visited the Bitterroot Valley, wrote that he never saw a white flower in a field of pink flowers. He believed the white-flowered locations "can hardly be numerous" and perhaps he is right, though especially in the area of Stevensville, Montana, white-flowered bitterroot are part of every population. Wiley was an astute observer and believed that "a yellow blossom might occur where there are white ones". He added that he was "still seeking such an extreme rarity among the Bitter Roots".[58]

In southwest Alberta, the flowers are all deep pink[59] and in northern Flathead County, all the flowers are, if anything, even a deeper pink to rose-red. No white flowers have been seen among the three Glacier County populations.

Plants at Craters of the Moon National Monument in Idaho are uniformly white-flowered with pink stamens and pistils. No rose-colored flowers are known within the monument, though they do occur nearby to the north. The local belief is that the chemical composition of the recent lava flows upon which the bitterroot grow is, in some way, responsible for the exclusively white-flowered plants. This is a possibility, but relict survival of a genetic strain and subsequent range expansion during and after the recent lava flows seems to be a better explanation.

The greatest color variation seems to be in the plants of the Bitterroot Valley. Here are found flowers of the purest white, a few of Watson's phase (the "yellow" bitterroot), pale pink to deep rose flowers and even a few of purple hue. No more fitting location could be found for this wide variation, since this was the ancestral home of the Flathead Indians, the tribe which was and is most closely associated with the bitterroot plant. Here also was the site of Meriwether Lewis's type collection of the species. The names of the valley, the river and the mountain range are taken from three languages; the *spatlum* of the Flathead, the *racine amere* of the trappers and traders and the bitterroot of the white settlers

GENETIC DIFFERENTIATION

Daubenmire raised bitterroot plants collected from five different locations: southwest British Columbia; near Wenatchee, Washington; Whitman County, Washington; near Columbus, Montana; and near Cody, Wyoming. The five sets of plants, raised at Pullman, Washington, showed "clear and consistent differences" in the timing of the various phases of annual growth and development. Strangely, though, these differences were unrelated to the day length or climate at the five locations.

Leaf rust attacked leaves of plants from one of the Washington locations and mice grazed Montana plants. All other plants from the various locations were immune both to rust and mice. Daubenmire interprets this as evidence of "local genetic differentiation".[60]

Bitterroot, at least in one northern Montana location, is of no interest to bears. Grizzly bears turn up bitterroot roots while foraging for other roots (chiefly *Lomatium macrocarpum* and *L. dissectum*) but leave the excavated *Lewisia* untouched. At the same site, chipmunks have been seen grazing spring bitterroot leaves but it does not seem to be a plant of top choice.[61]

Daubenmire's Montana and Wyoming plants retained green leaves at flowering time while plants from the other three locations were completely deciduous by the end of flowering.[62] This observation cannot be interpreted to imply that uncultivated native Montana and Wyoming plants retain their leaves at flowering. On the contrary, the vast majority of observed wild bitterroot plants in these states are leafless by flowering time. Cultivated plants receiving small but regular amounts of water tend to retain leaves throughout the flowering period.

The scattered distributions of bitterroot is a subject of perennial interest. Dispersal theories are limited only by the imagination of the curious observer. Following dispersal to widely scattered locations, populations separated from the main range of the species can undergo rapid genetic range in their isolation. Mechanisms readily develop that eventually can lead to the appearance of separate species.[63] Though there may be little apparent difference between the scattered populations, the possibility exists that there are actually multiple subspecies and it is conceivable that there are more than one species in the complex now known as *Lewisia rediviva*. *L. maguirei* and *L. disepala*, two closely related species, are both very restricted in their ranges and it is possible that they developed as isolated populations of a parent *Lewisia rediviva*. *Lewisia disepala*, as a matter of fact, originally was described in 1894 as *Lewisia rediviva* variety *yosemitiana* before Per Axel Rydberg classified it as a separate species in 1932.[64]

ENDNOTES

1. Marvel, p. 10-11.

2. Barr, p. 107.

3. Kuijt & Michener, p. 264.

4. Wilson, letter, 31 July 1990.

5. K. Wilson, "Bitterroots Babied," The *Missoulian*, n. d.

6. As a term, aeration is equal, perhaps preferable, to the term drainage. See Chap. 5, p. 64.

7. Daubenmire, p. 11.

8. Heath, p. 336-339. For years the consensus has been that *Lewisia tweedyi* is the most difficult of the genus to raise.

9. In arid North American locations, many plants are stimulated by the favorable temperatures and moisture of early autumn.

10. Marvel, p. 44. Another plant that estivates and resumes leaf growth in autumn is *Geum triflorum*, the well known prairie smoke of the plains.

11. Daubenmire, p. 17. Daubenmire's experiments took place in Pullman, Washington. The results cannot be applied to all wild populations of bitterroot.

12. Kirkwood, p. 47. J. E. Kirkwood was a botany professor at the University of Montana. The account related here took place sometime before 1916 in Missoula.

13. Hooker, 1863, Tab. 5395.

14. MONTU Herbarium, December, 1990.

15. Marvel, p. 45-51.

16. Marvel, p. 133.

17. Daubenmire, p. 19.

18. This resulted from observation of a garden plant from September to May at Pullman. Daubenmire, p. 18.

19. L. Clark, p. 120.

20. Mathew, p. 45.

21. Nuttall, 1834, p. 24. More concise is his Latin description, *"Flores magni, Cacti facie."*

22. U. S., 1871, p. 45. A few individual plants of the restricted *Lewisia maguirei* populations show this yellow-green color variation. Rarer still are plants with red-purple foliage.

23. June observations of 1990, 1991 and 1992. This phase at this location first reported by Mrs. Zach Bugli.

24. But only when grown apart. See Doonan, p. 195.

25. Daubenmire, p. 20.

26. Marvel, p. 35. This happened with many bitterroot at Craters of the Moon National Monument, Idaho, in June, 1991 and in northern Montana and southwestern Alberta in 1992.

27. Weber's calendar marks June 13 as "peak bloom of the Bitterroot flower" and June 26 as "Bitterroot flower in seed." B. Weber, 1985.

28. Daubenmire's term. Defined as the dried and twisted petals and stamens and considered as a unit.

29. Daubenmire, p. 16. Best conditions for germination would seem to be an early and constant snow cover beneath which the temperature would be a degree or two above freezing.

30. Mentioned in many places. An example, Nelson's "the roots are wonderfully tenacious of life," p. 48.

31. Four plants with leaves only were collected on 9 May 1991 in northern Glacier County, Montana. The roots were removed and the caudex and leaves were placed in damp sand. Buds appeared on all plants and on May 29, one root was excavated and found to be about one inch long. On July 24, one plant had three blooms and two other plants had one bloom each. No seed was produced and the plants died back. On September 15, tiny emergent leaves were noticed on two plants. On November 17, after -22°F, snow and a chinook that bared the ground, the leaves were still apparently alive. Tiny green leaves appeared on two plants in mid-March, 1992 but the plants did not survive the summer of 1992. See also Hogan, p. 52.

32. Daubenmire excavated 84 plants near Spokane, Washington. All but one had a single rosette. The exception had 38 caudices and did not flower. Daubenmire regarded it as a "teratologic specimen". Daubenmire, p. 14-15.

33. Daubenmire, p. 12.

34. Kirkwood, p. 47.

35. Daubenmire, p. 11.

36. Kartesz, 1, p. 202.

37. Hogan, p. 49.

38. Kuijt & Michener, p. 264. In 1982, the nearest known population was in the Elk River Valley of southeast B. C.

39. *Great Falls Tribune*, July 1, 1951, MHS File.

40. Kuijt & Michener, p. 266.

41. Wilson, *et al.*, p. 515.

42. Daubenmire, p. 21.

43. Barr, p. 107.

44. See Chap. 1, p. 3-4.

45. Vanderburg, 1991.

46. Suggested but not necessarily advocated by Malouf, in note, 1991.

47. On cultivation of native tobacco, see Davies, p. 47 quoting David Douglas and Hitchcock *et. al.*, 4, p. 285-86. Also, Turney-High, *Kutenai*, p. 172, and Johnson (ed.), p. 6-7.

48. Wilson, *et. al.*, p. 518.

49. For example, Kuijt letter, 19 Oct 1989.

50. These two alternatives are mentioned in Wilson, *et. al.*, p. 518, but for another Montana bitterroot location.

51. Wilson, *et al.*, p. 518-521.

52. Letter, Scotter, 9 March 1990.

53. Carrara, p. 27-34. Plant data secured by examining lake sediments immediately below both ash falls.

54. Wilson, *et. al.*, p. 518. Carrara, letter, 26 Nov 1986.

55. Carrara, p. 27.

56. Davidson, p. 14.

57. As well as in other Montana locations, notably near Helena.

58. Wiley, p. 269-70.

59. Kuijt & Michener, p. 266.

60. Daubenmire, p. 22.

61. Observations, northern Flathead County sites, 1989-1992.

62. Daubenmire, p. 22.

63. This is along the line suggested by Ernst Mayr's theory of peripatric speciation. See Mayr, p. 450.

64. Mathew, p. 54-57.

5
CULTIVATION AND MODERN USE

CULTIVATION

Of the nineteen species in the genus *Lewisia*, bitterroot was not only the first known to the western world, but also the first to be cultivated as a garden ornamental. William Jackson Hooker successfully grew the first flowering plant in 1863[1] from David Lyall's British Columbia collection. Apparently, the species caught on fast and in 1873, a person named Backhouse was awarded a First Class Certificate for his bitterroot by the Royal Horticultural Society in Great Britain.[2]

The genus *Lewisia* has long been popular in Britain and most plantsmen there are convinced they can grow them better than their American counterparts can.[3] English growers have more experience than Americans and they are particularly skilled in the raising of plants in alpine houses and in containers. Most members of the genus, including bitterroot, are well adapted to culture under cover where moisture can be strictly controlled. Some growers also believe that bitterroot can be grown to greater perfection in cultivation than in the wild since judicious feeding can bring on better flowering.[4] Skillful and patient gardeners, particularly in England, have achieved amazing results with potted *Lewisias*.[5] Most gardeners, however, have neither the ability nor the patience to match these results and the majority of bitterroots in gardens of the United States are left to flourish or perish untended.

Gardeners disagree over which of the lewisias is the most attractive garden subject. The argument comes down to two species, *Lewisia rediviva* and *L. tweedyi*. Leonard Wiley ranks bitterroot first[6] while H. Lincoln Foster writes that *L. tweedyi* is "without question the most beautiful of the lewisias and would rank near the top of any list of the best alpines in the world".[7] Brian Mathew hedges a bit and says that while bitterroot "is one of the most delightful and rewarding members of the genus," *L. tweedyi* "indeed is one of the most highly esteemed of all alpine plants".[8] Bitterroot is probably the easiest to grow while *L. tweedyi* has long been considered very difficult. Some modern gardeners, however, have apparently solved the early problems. A grower in Ontario, for example, uses *L. tweedyi* "in place of petunias to line paths".[9]

Personal preference and standards of beauty determine which is the most beautiful flower. *L. tweedyi* varies widely in flower color. Pink, deep apricot, orange, yellow, ivory and pure white variations (Reginald Farrer

Lewisia tweedyi. *Phil Pearson photo from
American Rock Garden Society.*

refers to "the most melting tones of apricot, salmon, cream and milk"[10]) are
known in flowers ranging up to three inches in diameter. An individual plant
of *L. tweedyi* is spectacular as no bitterroot ever is. Bitterroot, on the other
hand, is startling in its cactus-like appearance against a usually bare
background. It conveys the impression of an austere beauty rather than the
lushness characteristic of a floral display of *L. tweedyi*.

None of the lewisias, bitterroot included, is considered now to be a
difficult garden subject. All that is needed, one writer notes, is "a basic feel
for the native ecology and a few reliable horticultural techniques" and "any
one of the species can be grown to perfection".[11]

Bitterroot seeds germinate readily especially if the seeds are stratified.
Daubenmire's experiments leading to 100% germination followed keeping
seeds a degree or two above freezing for up to 90 days.[12] This requirement
is easily met by potting the seeds in a moist medium, then placing in the
refrigerator for a month or more. Germination in nature must be highly
variable depending upon annual weather conditions. Early snowfall, followed by a month or two of undiminished snow cover, is ideal as the
temperature beneath two or more feet of snow is a constant 32° to 34°F. In
eastern Washington (and elsewhere), bitterroot seeds germinate in November,[13] after a period of natural stratification. In some parts of its range,
seedlings do not appear until spring. Bitterroot seeds apparently remain
viable for many years.

After sprouting, seedlings can be kept covered under lights until spring,
then planted out. Lawrence Hills, an English grower, suggests the removal

of seed coats as soon as the seed leaves thrust upward. "It is a small detail," he writes, "but Lewisias repay attention to details".[14] Flowering occurs in the second year or later. Some gardeners prefer to place potted seeds outdoors (a time-honored tradition) subject to the "vagaries of the weather".[15] If enough seeds are sown, there always will be some germination, but it will be neither as rapid nor as certain as the indoor method. Where bitterroot can be grown outdoors without protection, seed can be planted in the fall where the plants are intended to grow. Seedlings seem to be completely hardy. Seeds planted outdoors in southwest Alberta in October of 1991, for example, germinated and produced visible leaves in February of 1992. They survived -9°F with no snow cover on 11 April and -10°F in mid-May. Spring planting of unstratified seeds almost invariably results in failure.[16]

Attempted cultivation of bitterroot in unprotected outdoor gardens in some parts of the United States likewise is doomed to failure. One such unfavorable area is the Pacific Northwest west of the Cascades. There, the effect of summer rains and fog may in rare cases be overcome by absolutely perfect drainage, but only in exceptional years. Generally, bitterroot is "unadaptable to cultivation" in, for example, the Seattle area.[17]

In Britain, bitterroot almost always is grown in clay pots plunged in sand and roofed by alpine houses or frames. One writer "questions whether outdoor cultivation is even possible, but it is easily grown in pots if overwatering is avoided".[18] The most up-to-date word from Britain is that the deciduous species are "not at all easy to grow outside . . . as a result they are most often seen cosseted in the close confines of the alpine house".[19]

Bitterroot in pot, Southwest Alberta.

Alpine houses and container gardening are gaining in popularity in the United States, but most gardeners still prefer to take a chance with bitterroot and plant it outdoors unprotected. Temperature extremes have little or no effect, but summer moisture can be fatal. Moisture should be excluded as much as possible after flowering and good drainage is essential. The effect of summer rains in some areas can be compensated for by excellent drainage, either by depth of porous medium or by growing plants on steeply-angled beds. Most casualties are probably caused by crown rot and authorities agree that the crown of bitterroot plants should rest on scree and never on soil.[20]

The term "drainage" and the horticultural concepts derived from it recently have been critically examined. Since the literature on the genus *Lewisia* invariably is involved with the subject of drainage, this new view must be considered. "The word drainage is like a drumbeat punctuating every paragraph," writes Norman C. Deno. "What is critical is the supply or more precisely the pressure of oxygen. The word *drainage* should be crossed out throughout the horticultural literature and replaced by the word *aeration* . . . It can be added that if drainage were essential, plants could never be grown by hydroponics."[21]

Since the hallowed concept of "good drainage" undoubtedly will die hard, its substitution by "good aeration" is a long way off. Deno is right, though it should be pointed out that this oxygenation requirement has long been recognized, particularly with alpine plants.[22]

It is not surprising that bitterroot is easily grown in and around Missoula, Montana, and in the Bitterroot Valley. In that part of Montana, wild bitterroot are still found on dry hillsides that are completely surrounded by suburban developments and some bitterroot populations have survived a century and more of continuous stock grazing.[23] The Bitterroot Valley, including the hills and ridges near Missoula, was historically the most productive and most intensely harvested bitterroot area known. Apparently, the climate of southwest Montana is well suited to the requirements of bitterroot and, in addition, the prevalent soil types drain and aerate well.

Propagation of bitterroot by division is possible but rarely done. Farrer long ago recognized the major concern when he wrote that "a well-established clump is by far too lovely and precious"[24] to chop up. The standard method of vegetative propagation consists of notching the rim of the caudex in spring, which, ideally, leads to the development of a growing point at each notch. A year later, the caudex and root are cut lengthwise and each growing point planted out separately.[25] Vegetative propagation usually is restricted to the cotyledon section of the genus and then only for the purpose of increasing stocks of sterile hybrids.

Many of the mature plants in gardens today, particularly in the United States, have been transplanted directly from the wild. While this is a subject that is sure to generate disagreement,[26] there now seems to be no good reason for wholesale harvesting to accommodate the commercial trade. Undoubt- edly, the great majority of transplants perish either due to placement under climatic conditions where they cannot grow or because of inattention. Therefore, it is best to raise bitterroot (and other wild flowers) from seed or from stock purchased from approved nurseries. An exception can be made to condone collection of distinctive variants[27] but only if carefully and conscientiously done.

Most rock gardeners (and it is usually rock gardeners who struggle with bitterroot) rarely use fertilizers as there is an ancient and persistent belief that feeding changes the character of compact and tidy plants and turns them into lush sprawling masses of leaves. Bitterroot grown in pots must be fed, particularly if the plants are not repotted frequently. This has been proven many times, especially in Britain, where the cultivation of plants in containers has produced individual plants that no outdoor garden can rival.[28]

Certain members of the genus *Lewisia* are famous for hybridizing in gardens. Most of the crossing involves *Lewisia cotyledon* in all three varieties and *L. brachycalyx*. Some crossing is intentional and eagerly sought whereas other mixing seems to be an inevitable result of congenial affiliation of various species in proximity.

No record exists of bitterroot crossing in nature. In cultivation, it has been crossed with *Lewisia cotyledon* on at least three occasions, with *L. columbiana* and with *L. longipetala*.[29] According to reports, it also will cross with *L. brachycalyx*.[30] None of the hybrids have produced seed so all reproduction has been carried on by vegetative propagation. Probably the only species of the genus that has not been crossed and that seems "determined to remain virtuous"[31] is *L. tweedyi*. Part of the reason for this "reluctance" is the very high chromosome count of 2n=92-95 in *L. tweedyi*. Of the species that have been crossed, the chromosome count ranges from 2n=20 in *L. brachycalyx* to 2n=28 in *L. rediviva* and *L. cotyledon* to 2n=30 in *L. columbiana*.[32]

HENRY GRANT

One of the most successful growers of bitterroot is Henry Grant of Hamilton, Montana. His garden dates from 1957 and contains hundreds of plants ranging in color from pure white to purple. Mr. Grant distinguishes seven shades of red among his bitterroots with rose-colored flowers predominating. Pure white plants are found in the Grant garden as well as a few of the "yellow" Watson's phase. Intermediates of every possible variation occur. Very rare is a dark-hued plant with purplish flowers.

Most plants in the Grant garden are extremely robust with up to 60 or 70 flowers per plant. Many of these plants still bear leaves at flowering while wild plants in Montana are almost always leafless at anthesis. This robustness and the presence of leaves at flowering undoubtedly result from light watering throughout the growing and flowering period and perhaps

Robust bitterroot, Henry Grant garden, Hamilton, Montana.

Bitterroot in cultivation, Henry Grant garden, Hamilton, Montana.

from a light feeding of dry manure in the fall. Lack of competition also contributes to greater development of individual plants.

Plants raised from seed in the Grant garden produce a bloom or two in the second year and reach optimum flowering within another year or two. Foliage variations, such as the differences between Watson's phase and typical bitterroot, are not apparent until the second year from seed.

Peak bloom is usually reached in mid-June though atypical weather can cause early or late blooming. In 1992, a year of erratic weather, the Grant garden was about two weeks "ahead" with the first blooms appearing near the middle of May. In Daubenmire's garden at Pullman, Washington, fully opened flowers were present from May 23 to July 1[33] for an unstated number of years before 1974. Daubenmire's plants were collected from widely scattered locations in Washington, British Columbia, south central Montana and northwestern Wyoming, so it is very possible that several genetic strains were present.

BITTERROOT DAY

"Bitterroot Day" is annually celebrated in the old courthouse museum in Hamilton. The date varies with the blooming of bitterroot and in 1992, Bitterroot Day fell on May 31, one of the earliest, if not the earliest day on record. Bitterroot flowers from Henry Grant's garden -- in 1992, some 700-800 blossoms -- are displayed in the museum and Mr. Grant purveys potted plants from the back of his pickup truck. He reports that customers prefer

Henry Grant and Karen Feather, Bitterroot Day, 1992.

the deep rose-red flowers and are only slightly interested in the white bitterroot.

At one time, tasting of bitterroot roots was part of the annual affair. Author Dayton Duncan attended a Bitterroot Day and reported negatively on his Hamilton tasting experience. He noted that *Lewisia rediviva* was named "in honor of the man who couldn't stomach it," a reference to Lewis's report that the root was "naucious to my pallate" on 22 August 1805. Duncan wrote that the root must be peeled and then boiled for at least 35 minutes. Sampling several preparations, he found all bitter and unpalatable.[34] He probably ate the roots of flowering plants which would have been bitter no matter how prepared.

Photographic exhibits of Indians and of the gathering of bitterroot, along with paintings, decorated china, poetry and other art work complete the display. Henry Grant, in his bitterroot shirt, is a prominent figure at Bitterroot Day and much of the success of the day can be attributed to his participation.

THREATS

The greatest threat to bitterroot populations is loss of habitat. As long ago as 1948, Leonard Wiley recognized the "rapid habitat loss" in the vicinity of Missoula.[35] Two years later, a Hamilton reporter wrote that "encroachment of cultivated land" together with the expanding presence of Russian knapweed and "other tramps" were causing the loss of much bitterroot from historic grounds.[36] Since that time, suburban development has eradicated far more bitterroot than anyone could have predicted, though the destruction of habitat by the monocultural march of knapweed and leafy spurge is perhaps a greater threat. Particularly in the Bitterroot Valley, no native plant seems capable of resisting the domination of these two alien species.

A lesser, but still significant threat, is the loss caused by indiscriminate collecting. Plant societies and environmental groups have adopted standards of ethics that condemn practically all harvesting of live plants in the wild but they cannot control the depredations of unprincipled collectors. Some species of *Lewisia* in the Pacific northwest were heavily harvested years ago "reducing some populations [particularly of *L. cotyledon*] to unacceptably low levels".[37] Other unspecified species were reported to be "nearly exterminated . . . by root-diggers for the rock garden trade".[38] Genetic strains and certain variants of bitterroot undoubtedly have been lost from the wild over the years as collectors gathered them for the horticultural trade. Old time collectors argue that they are actually saving the variants and preserving genetic diversity, but many disagree with them. It is a long standing argument.

BITTERROOT AND MONTANA

Bitterroot is more closely identified with Montana than with any other state. This identification goes back many years. One Montana contribution to the Columbian Exposition of Chicago in 1893 was a "scientific floral exhibit," including bitterroot, under the direction of F. D. Kelsey.[39] Another and separate contribution, entitled the "Montana Women's World's Fair Collection," included an array of 416 mounted plant specimens, many of them bitterroot, from various Montana locations.[40]

This patriotic interest led to a vigorous campaign in 1894 to designate the bitterroot as Montana's state flower. Genevieve Murray reported the results in detail 35 years later. In a ballot that drew 5857 votes, bitterroot led with 3621, followed far back by evening primrose, then wild rose, white clematis, cactus, goldenrod and mariposa lily. The bitterroot "lobby" was undoubtedly well-organized. Missoula County produced 1630 votes, more than any other county, with 1293 going for bitterroot. Ravalli, another county where the bitterroot is abundant (Hamilton the county seat), registered 608 votes for bitterroot of a total of 644. Flathead County, where little or no bitterroot was known in 1894, produced only one vote and it went to bitterroot. Lewis and Clark County (Helena the county seat, as well as the state capitol and not great bitterroot country) mustered only 87 votes but with a majority going to bitterroot. A bill was introduced, passed without dissent, and signed into law by Governor John E. Rickards in 1895. According to Murray, there was some statewide discussion in 1919 suggesting a change "to some flower more commonly seen, the kinnikinnick receiving favorable comment." But kinnikinnick, a widespread species, was not "distinctively Montanan, and all discussions came to naught".[41] Professor J. E. Kirkwood of the University of Montana wrote that bitterroot had been "well chosen." He cited its "beauty and grace" and its abundance in Montana over that in any other state. He went on to note "the part it played in the sustenance of the primitive races and the early pioneers, its discovery by Lewis and Clark and the fact that its name is borne by one of the noblest mountain ranges of the state". Bitterroot, he concluded, "in its humble way suggests the moral qualities of purity, hardihood and vigor".[42]

The popularity of bitterroot as an artistic subject has extended to many media. In the late nineteenth century, legislators' desks in Helena were embellished with hand-carved patterns of bitterroot flowers. At the turn of the century, a carload of table linen with a bitterroot motif was manufactured in Belfast, Ireland. Reportedly, it was all shipped to Butte and was very popular.[43] Much of it surely still survives. Floral bitterroot designs are found on china (many examples in the museum at Hamilton), pillows, bedspreads, tapestries, stationery and every other conceivable object of art. Watercolorists and sketchers particularly find bitterroot to be a favorite subject. On a more mundane note, many Montana road maps feature a stylized bitterroot with the flowers and leaves appearing (inaccurately) together. Bitterroot postcards, usually photographic reproductions and therefore accurate, are very popular. Many Montana books, especially those dealing with plants, are identified with a bitterroot design or photograph. As time passes and bitterroot populations diminish, the plant becomes increasingly popular as a symbol of the state of Montana. Perhaps it is time, as a Hamilton editorial urged in 1956, to set aside a Bitterroot State Park before the "progress of civilization, the breaking of the soil, the encroachment of fields upon the meadows of nature"[44] cause the disappearance of *spatlem/racine amere*/bitterroot from all but the most remote locations.

ENDNOTES

1. Some writers (Saunders, p. 27; Elrod n. p.) state that 1826 was the year of introduction. That was the year when Hooker tried, unsuccessfully, to cultivate Douglas's collection.

2. Mathew, p. 142. Backhouse had a nursery at York and, in 1887, a colored illustration was drawn from his flowering bitterroot. *The Garden*, p. 124.

3. For example, Ingwersen, p. 68.

4. Wiley, p. 273.

5. Royton Heath "grew on" a 12-inch pot of what he called *Lewisia howellii* (now considered a variety of *L. cotyledon*) to such perfection that it won three awards, including best plant in show, in one year. The container, Heath wrote, "must have had fully two thousand flowers when fully out, and as it can be imagined it presented a charming sight," p. 336.

6. Wiley, p. 234.

7. Foster, p. 269.

8. Mathew, p. 34; p. 123.

9. Porteous, p. 52.

10. Farrer, I, p. 449.

11. Hogan, p. 47.

12. Daubenmire, p. 16.

13. Ibid.

14. Hills, p. 324.

15. The custom in Britain according to Mathew, p. 28-9.

16. K. Williams, n. p.

17. Hitchcock and Cronquist, 2, p. 235.

18. Elliott, p. 74.

19. Mathew, p. 28.

20. For example, Elliott, p. 68, p. 74; Colley and Mineo, p. 44; Wiley, p. 272.

21. Deno, p. 34.

22. Summarized in DeSanto, p. 2-3.

23. But not the invasion of exotic species such as leafy spurge (*Euphorbia esula*) and knapweed (*Centaurea spp.*). Bitterroot competes with these species for a while but eventually is displaced.

24. Farrer, I, p. 449.

25. Mathew, p. 30; Hogan, p. 52.

26. Reginald Farrer (d. 1920), one of the great old-time collectors, harvested immense numbers of plants in Europe and Asia. "Those who love and know the flowers of the alps as only those of long and arduous experience can hope to do [Farrer undoubtedly includes himself here], -- those, of all people, are not to be accused of 'devastating' the ranges and exterminating rare plants," he wrote, adding later, "The essentials are a due reverence, and a straight downward drive, about five inches away from the plant, with a long and narrow flat fern-trowel, made all in one piece." Farrer, I, p. liii-lv.

27. For example, Foster writes, "under many circumstances it is perfectly proper and even desirable to bring into the garden plants collected in the wild," p. 108.

28. Royton Heath is a leader in this field. Writing of the "fallacy" of starving alpines [and bitterroot can be included here] he states, "This is utter rot and I would like to kill it once and for all", p. 114.

29. Elliott, p. 68; Parizek, p. 195-96.

30. Mathew, p. 131-32.

31. As Joe Elliott says in R. C. Elliott, p. 73.

32. Elliott, p. 66; Mathew, p. 24-25.

33. Daubenmire, p. 20.

34. Duncan, p. 294.

35. Wiley, p. 267.

36. *Great Falls Tribune*, Parade, p. 16-17, 23 May 1950.

37. Mathew, p. 17.

38. W. Weber, p. 413.

39. Kelsey's name is preserved by *Kelseya uniflora* (Wats.) Rydberg, a compact cushion plant of the rose family and the floral emblem of the Montana Native Plant Society.

40. Murray, p. 28-30.

41. Murray, p. 37-39. The (Hamilton) *Bitter Root Times*, on 12 October 1894, took the opportunity to brag of its 644 votes while noting that Lewis and Clark County, "with all her boasted culture, only managed to cast 87".

42. Kirkwood, p. 46.

43. These stories from Murray, p. 39-40.

44. The (Hamilton) *Western News*, 5 April 1956, MHS Folder.

APPENDIX I

ETHNOBOTANY OF LEWIS AND CLARK EXPEDITION (USE OF ROOTS)

In his instructions to Meriwether Lewis, President Thomas Jefferson ordered his secretary to learn of the "food, clothing, and domestic accomodations" of "the people inhabiting the line you will pursue". He further charged Lewis to become acquainted with "the soil and face of the country; its growth and vegetable productions, especially those not of the United States".[1] These instructions alone undoubtedly would have encouraged Lewis and Clark to bring back thorough notes on the subject of useful plants. Their interest, however, came to have a much more practical application when they were forced to rely on several species of edible roots to carry them through hard times in the mountains of the west.

Jefferson admitted that Lewis was "not regularly educated". "But," he wrote, "he possesses a great mass of accurate observation on all the subjects of nature which present themselves here, and will, therefore readily select those only in his new route which shall be new".[2] Lewis may have received botanical training from Dr. Benjamin Smith Barton, the foremost American botanist of the time.[3] If he did not, Jefferson's example and knowledge together would have been sufficient to stimulate a strong amateur interest in the enthusiastic young captain. As important as a professional botanist may have been to the expedition, Lewis's thoroughness and dedication overcame his few shortcomings. His botanical observations are almost always perceptive and reliable.[4]

William Clark, who honestly admitted to "slender bottonical skill,"[5] had one necessary attribute of a good field botanist: he was a conscientious keeper of records. Many of his plant observations were copied from Lewis's journals, but when he was apart from Lewis and when he alone kept the expedition's journal, he was diligent and observant. More than anything else, he was the cartographer and geographer, not the natural scientist. He was also, as Paul Russell Cutright wrote, "highly successful in meeting the demands of actual living".[6] "Actual living" often required attention to the task of finding something to eat.

Much has been written of the amicable joint leadership of Lewis and Clark. They were different in many ways, but it seemed their differences worked in positive ways with no dissent. Cutright's description of Lewis as a "dreamer, intent, fine-drawn, reserved, unwavering, generally humorless" is balanced by that of Clark as "warm, companionable, a good judge of men, an easy conversationalist".[7]

In his introduction to the *Journals* in 1904, Reuben Gold Thwaites recognized "the poetic temperament of Lewis, who loved flowers and animals, and in his notes discussed like a philosopher who enjoyed the exercise of writing". Clark, on the other hand, "spelled phonetically, capitalized chaotically, and occasionally slipped in his grammar".[8]

Readers of the journals are delighted by the prose of Clark. His straightforward descriptions and "often amusingly eccentric orthography"[9] are part of many memorable passages. Typical is his comment on a rapid weather change. "In this Situation we Continued about 40 Minits," he wrote on 14 July 1804, "when the Storm Sudenly Seased and the river became Instancetaniously as Smoth as Glass". When he saw the abundance of wildlife along the Yellowstone River in 1806, he wrote, "for me to mention or give an estimate of the differant Species of wild animals on the river particularly Buffalow, Elk Antelopes & Wolves would be increditable. I shall therefore be silent on the subject further". He followed, as he often did, with a practical observation: "So it is we have a great abundance of the best of meat".

Lewis's dreamy "seens of visionary inchantment" along the Missouri on 31 May 1805 is often quoted. Reaching what is now Lemhi Pass on the Continental Divide, he wrote, "The road took us to the most distant fountain of the waters of the Mighty Missouri in surch of which we have spent so many toilsome days and wristless nights. thus far I had accomplished one of those great objects on which my mind has been unalterably fixed for many years, judge then of the pleasure I felt in allying my thirst with this pure and ice-cold water . . .".[10]

•   •   •

While at Camp Dubois during the winter of 1803-04, Lewis wrote a note on three species of plants used by the Indians as food. These were identified by Dr. William Trelease, Director of the Missouri Botanical Garden, as *Nelumbo lutea* ("unmistakably"), *Ipomoea pandurata* ("probably") and *Nymphaea reniformis* ("probably").

Nelumbo was used by the Kickapoos, said Lewis, and called *Po-kish'-a-co-mah*. From it, they prepared an "agreeable dish . . . esteemed as nutricius as the pumpkin or squash and is not very dissimilar in taste". The French residents also used the roots of *Nelumbo*, knowing it, according to Lewis, as *"Pois de Shicoriat"* or *"Graine de Volais"*. A modern text states that *Nelumbo*, or American lotus, was extensively used as food and makes "a palatable dish".[11]

Ipomoea, a morning glory, was known to Lewis as the "common wild pittatoe". Since many plant roots were described by Lewis and Clark as resembling or as tasting like a potato or sweet potato, this is not a conclusive identification clue. This root was dried, pounded and made into bread -- also "agreeable". H. D. Harrington wrote that a related species, *Ipomoea leptophylla*, was "one of the best plants we have ever tried . . .".[12]

A recent opinion on this "common wild pittatoe" is that it was *Apios americana*, commonly known as Indian potato, ground nut or potato bean.[13] Dr. Edwin Palmer referred to a species of *Apios* as the "true *pomme de terre* of the French" and wrote that it was (in 1870 and before) "extensively used as an article of diet".[14]

The pond lily, *Nymphaea*, was not seen by Lewis before he wrote his description. He learned, though, that the raw roots were not only disagreeable, but decidedly dangerous. "A small quantity will kill a hog," he wrote, "yet prepared by the Indians it makes not only an agreeable but a nutricious food". The root was boiled after drying and either eaten with meat or made into a bread. Trelease's identification is only tentative and this plant also could have been a species of pond lily now included in the genus *Nuphar*. *Nymphaea tuberosa*, however, was probably the plant mentioned by Lewis.[15] It no longer occurs in Missouri.[16]

• • •

In a notebook separate from the expedition journals, Lewis described two plants seen in 1804. One, *Hydrastis canadensis* (yellowroot), was known in Kentucky and elsewhere and usually was used as a remedy to cure "sore eyes". Lewis wrote also that "this root is a fine aromatic bitter . . . it is probable that it might be applied internally in many cases as a medecine with good effect . . . It makes an excellent mouth water". Yellowroot, also known as goldenseal, is still a popular herbal remedy. The root of the second plant was valued as a "strong stomatic stimelent, and frequently used in sperits with bitter herbs". Trelease identified this plant as wild ginger (*Asarum canadense* or *A. reflexum*).[17] Lewis was later to use roots of a species of wild ginger as a poultice on John Potts's inflamed and swollen leg. Potts "found great relief".

• • •

After the departure from Camp Dubois in May of 1804, the first mention in the journals of an edible root is found on July 10 when Clark, along the Kansas River, described a "butifull bottom Plain . . . covered with wild rye

and Potatoes". Thwaites identified the potatoes as *Psoralea*
esculenta, the ground apple or
pomme de terre of the plains.[18]
Clark mentioned it a few other
times in the summer of 1804
and on 8 May 1805, Lewis
wrote a long description of the
plant. The expedition was then
at the junction of the Milk and
Missouri Rivers. Lewis wrote
of how the Indians pounded
the dried roots to a powder,
then used it to "thicken their
soope". The Indians boiled the
roots whole or mashed them
with fat and berries to make
something like a "haisty pud-
ding". Lewis thought this an
"agreeable dish". The white
apple, he wrote, "appears to
me a tasteless insippid food of
itself, tho' I have no doubt but
it is a very healthy and moder-

The ground apple or pomme de terre
(Psoralea esculenta).

ately nutricious food". He recommended it to "our epicures" as it would
"serve them in their ragouts and gravies in stead of the truffles morella". (A
year later, Lewis ate morel mushrooms, without salt or grease, and described them as "truly an insippid taistless food".) He was surprised to find
that the Indians could eat large quantities of the raw root of *Psoralea*
"without sustaining any inconvenience or injury therefrom".

In June of 1805, Sacagawea fell mysteriously ill. Lewis doctored her,
using "barks and opium" together with mineral water and employing the
common treatment of bleeding. She was permitted to take only broiled
buffalo and meat broth. On this diet, she appeared to be on the road to
recovery, but her husband, Charbonneau, allowed her to eat a meal of raw
Psoralea roots and dried fish. She immediately became ill again and Lewis
believed this relapse was due to the diet change. This was Lewis's first
experience with unpleasant effects of raw roots and he was to be ever wary
of them.

Psoralea esculenta was of much importance to the Indians of the Great
Plains.[19] On the westbound journey, Lewis and Clark ate little of it,
preferring to dine on the fat buffalo which were so abundant. But on the way
home, Clark's party "dug [a] great parcel of the roots which the Nativs call

Hankee and the engagees the white apple which they boiled and made use of with their meat, this is a large insipid root and very tasteless. the nativs use the root after it is dry and pounded in their Scup".

• • •

While at Fort Mandan in December of 1804, Clark mentioned a root "Discribed by Mr. Henry[20] for the Cure of a Mad Dog". He again wrote of the plant two months later and described its use. Also a remedy for snake bite, "The way of useing it is to scarify the part when bitten to chu or pound an inch or more if the root is Small. and applying it to the bitten part renewing it twice a Day, the bitten person is not to chaw nor Swallow any of the Root for it might have contrary effect". Lewis also mentioned that the plant and specimens with roots were collected to send to Jefferson. This collection was among those lost, so positive identification cannot be made. Neither Elliott Coues nor Thwaites attempted an identification, but Cutright has suggested the plant may have been purple coneflower (*Echinacea angustifolia*).[21] Jeff Hart reports that *E. pallida* (synonymous with *E. angustifolia*) was known as "an antidote for rattlesnake and other venemous bites, stings, and poisonous conditions".[22] Alex Johnston says that roots of *E. angustifolia* were chewed by Indians of eastern Montana to take away the pain of toothache.[23] In the most recent edition of the *Journals*, Gary Moulton, with no more information, positively identified the plant as *E. angustifolia*.[24] It is a good guess that the roots Lewis described as "highly prized by the natives as a efficatious remidy in cases of the bite of the rattle Snake or Mad Dog" were indeed of the purple cone flower. Derivatives of parts of *Echinacea* species are popular herbal remedies in general use today.

• • •

As a genus of plants, onions would have been familiar and undoubtedly welcome to the largely carnivorous party. Aside from 193 pounds of portable soup (ingredients unknown), dry "beens" and "pees", cornmeal and flour, the only vegetable products brought along were preserved apples.[25] Lewis first noted onions on 12 April 1805 along the Missouri, finding them "agreeable,"[26] and did not mention them again until July 22 when he "met with great quantities of a smal onion" on an island (which he named Onion Island) of the Missouri. The onion was "white crisp and well flavored" and Lewis thought it "as pleasantly flavored as any species of that root I ever tasted". Considering the time and place of collection, *Allium cernuum*, the well known and attractive nodding onion, seems to be the best guess. *A. textile*, a plant of drier habitats, would also fit the "white crisp and well flavored" description. The party collected more onions the next day and Lewis noted the presence of "a species of garlic also which grows on the high lands with a flat leaf now green and in blos. but is strong tough and disagreeable." Coues thinks this may have been *A. geyeri* and Moulton says it was "possibly" *A. brevistylum*.[27]

Chives (*A. schoenoprasum*) would have been known to expedition members as the wild form is identical to the cultivated chives of eighteenth century gardens. Lewis tasted some on 29 March 1806 and found them "as quite agreeably flavored as the chives". The identification is tentative since the plant would not yet have been in flower.[28]

On the return journey, Lewis sampled another onion "exceedingly crisp and delicately flavoured indeed I think more sweet and less strong than any I ever taisted". Coues identified this as *A. tolmiei*, a logical guess. This identification has been accepted by Thwaites and Cutright but both with reservation. Moulton notes that it was either *A. tolmiei* or *A. douglasii*.[29]

Other mentions of onions lack identification by early commentators. The expedition found them near the Pacific coast and on into Idaho along the Kooskooskee [Clearwater] River on their return route. Along the Clearwater, they boiled small onions which acted as an "antidote to the effects of others".[30] This was especially welcome as the men had been suffering from gas and "griping" due to their diet of camas and cous roots.

Despite its familiarity and its use in many places, the genus *Allium* is poorly represented in Lewis and Clark's collections. For some reason, few specimens were collected and those that were brought east were partially eaten by museum beetles.[31]

•   •   •

"Wild liquorice" was first mentioned by Lewis on 8 May 1805 near the junction of the Milk and Missouri Rivers, but he made no mention of its use. More than a year later, he wrote that "the wild liquorice and sunflower are very abundant in the plains and river bottoms". He was then near the Sweet Grass Hills close to the 8 May 1805 location and, again, no mention is made of any use.

While at Fort Clatsop, however, the expedition members ate the root of a plant "much resembling the common liquorice in taste and Size". Later, they secured more of these roots which Clark referred to as "a kind of Licquirish which they rost in embers and call *Cul-ho-mo*". Writing of "the liquorice of this country [at Fort Clatsop]", Lewis noticed no difference between it and the plant "cultivated in our gardens". He goes on to say the native root "when roasted possesses an agreeable flavour not unlike the sweet pittaitoe".

The plant noticed by Lewis on the plains of Montana was undoubtedly *Glycrrhiza lepidota*, which is similar to *G. glabra*, the licorice of eastern gardens and of commerce. The "liquorice" roots eaten at Fort Clatsop have been identified by Thwaites as *Lupinus littoralis*,[32] relying on David Douglas's description of 1825. Douglas wrote that Lewis and Clark's wild licorice contained "a large quantity of farinaceous substance, and it is a very meritous wholesome food". The lupine that he describes, however, does not correspond to *Lupinus littoralis* though he did collect *L. littoralis* among 17 species of lupine.[33] This confusion was increased by Coues's identification of Lewis's "liquorice of this country" as *Glycrrhiza lepidota*[34] even though this plant is not known in the vicinity of Fort Clatsop.

There seems to be no positive solution to this puzzle when it is assumed that Lewis knew *Glycrrhiza glabra*, the plant of gardens in the eastern United States. He would not have confused the similar pinnately-leaved and yellow-flowered *G. lepidota* with the palmately-leaved, purple-flowered *Lupinus littoralis* of the Fort Clatsop area. *G. lepidota* is mentioned in Pursh's *Flora*[35] from Lewis's collections as are two species of *Lupinus,* but all of these are neither coastal nor edible.[36] Despite Lewis's statement that he observed "no difference" in the root he ate from that "cultivated in our gardens", he must have been mistaken. Though the relevant passage is confusing, he apparently never saw an entire plant of *Lupinus littoralis*. Thus the only conclusion that can be made now is that the coastal plant was not *Glycrrhiza lepidota*. If it was *Lupinus littoralis* — as it seems to have been — Douglas's description ("flowers faint white; leaves alternate, linear, sessile . . .")[37] defies explanation. *Glycrrhiza* roots, it should be pointed out, are a source of extract and generally not used as food.[38]

• • •

During the summer of 1805, the expedition traveled over the Great Plains and did not cross the Continental Divide until late August. Along the route, they were almost always in good hunting country and so relied little, if any, on native vegetation to supplement their diet. Their guide for what little use they made of roots, berries and other edible plant parts was undoubtedly Sacagawea. To a much lesser extent, they may have been advised by Touissant Charbonneau (usually Shabono or Chabono in the *Journals*), George Drouillard (invariably Drewyer) and Peter Cruzatte. Sacagawea recognized familiar country on the upper Missouri and it can be assumed she became more knowledgeable of local plants in the same area.

On 22 August 1805, Drouillard became involved in a minor altercation with Shoshone Indians along the Jefferson River. The Indians ran off, leaving their baggage to Drouillard. Included were three parcels of roots, one identified by Coues as bitterroot (*Lewisia rediviva*) and another as "something like" *Helianthus tuberosus*.[39] The third may have been *Perideridia gairdneri*, commonly known as yampa. All would have been known to Sacagawea.

Bitterroot was distasteful to Lewis and he "transferred them to the Indians who had eat them heartily". The second root, "something like the smallest of the Jerusalem artichoke," was "certainly the best root I [Lewis] have yet seen in uce among the Indians". Lewis thought this root preferable to Jerusalem artichoke (presumably he referred to *Helianthus tuberosus*, known at the time in cultivation) "however there is some allowance to be made for the length of time I have now been without vegitable food to which I was always much attatched". In June of the following year, Lewis "met with a plant," which he described in some detail and which, he wrote, "formed one of those collections of roots which Drewyer took from the Shoshones last summer on the head of Jefferson's river". Lewis's description was enough for C. V. Piper to identify the plant as *Claytonia lanceolata* (western springbeauty), one of the best of edible roots.[40]

Spring beauty (Claytonia lanceolata).

While at Fort Mandan in October of 1804, Clark had written of a "large Been" which the mice of the prairie discover and collect. The Indians searched out these hoards and robbed them, though they usually left something so the mice would survive to collect other hoards. In the following spring, Sacagawea dug up hoards cached by ground squirrels or gophers (and perhaps mice) and secured a "good quantity". Lewis thought they tasted like Jerusalem artichokes though the plant was much smaller than the *Helianthus tuberosus* he knew. Nevertheless, Coues stated that this was *H. tuberosus*.[41] Moulton, however, says this was *Amphicarpa bracteata*, the hog peanut, and that Lewis had confused the methods of collecting it and *H. tuberosus*.[42]

In March of 1805, Clark described what may have been another plant when he wrote "the Indians raise a kind of artichoke, which they say is common in the prairies, it is well tasted". Possibly this was Nuttall sunflower (*Helianthus nuttallii*) because of "the similarity in root shape and taste" (as Moulton writes) to that of Jerusalem artichoke.[43] But *Claytonia lanceolata* roots are also similar in shape and taste to *H. tuberosus* so, at this time, it is impossible to say for sure what the root was. Whatever it was, Jerusalem artichoke is still cultivated as it was long before the time of Lewis and Clark.

The third root confiscated by Drouillard on 22 August 1805 was almost certainly *Perideridia gairdneri*, variously known generically as *Peucedanum, Carum* or *Anethum* and commonly as yampa. Lewis described a dried root only, but his comment that "this rout is frequently eaten by the Indians either green or in it's dryed state without the preparation of boiling" led Thwaites to conclude it was yampa. This root also has been identified as *Valeriana edulis* (edible valerian), despite Lewis's observation that the root was eaten both fresh and cooked. According to H. D. Harrington, the Indians "considered the raw roots [of valerian] to be poisonous, which may well be the case".[44] John Charles Frémont wrote that the root of valerian had a "very strong and remarkably peculiar taste and odor". It was "extremely offensive" to some people and was "characterized by Mr. Preuss [cartographer Charles Preuss] as the most horrid food he had ever put in his mouth". Nevertheless, it was "full of nutriment". Frémont also stated that vale-

Yampa or "Fennel" (Perideridia gairdneri).

rian was poisonous when raw and that it had to be cooked for two days to render it fit for consumption.[45]

A few days later, Lewis watched Shoshone women collecting "the root of a speceis of fennel . . . and feeding their poor starved children". He followed with an accurate description of yampa in leaf and flower. Coues then identified the plant as *Carum* (later *Perideridia*) *gairdneri* and noted that "the fascicled tubers are an important article of food with various tribes of Indians".[46]

Both Lewis and Clark considered yampa one of the most useful and desirable of all wild roots. On 16 May 1806, Lewis found it (as usual) "very agreeable food . . . and they dispell the wind which the roots called cows and quamash are apt to create". On the same date, Clark wrote "Shabonos Squar [Sacagawea] gathered a quantity of *fenel* roots which we find very paliatiable and nurushing food". Sacagawea later collected a store of these roots to help the expedition through the Bitterroot Mountains on the return journey. Yampa had the advantage of being, as Clark wrote, "very paliatiable either fresh rosted boiled or dried".

Most writers on native plants agree that yampa is the best, or one of the best, of all native roots. C. V. Piper called it "the finest food plant of the northwestern Indians" and noted their "sweet nutty flavor".[47] Lewis J. Clark wrote "they are delicious either baked like miniature sweet potatoes, or fried in butter. There is general agreement that these are the best flavoured and most nutritious of the native plant foods."[48] Jeff Hart agrees, writing that "'Indian carrot' roots probably taste better than any other wild roots found in Montana".[49]

Nutritionally, yampa ranks ahead of Jerusalem artichoke (*Helianthus tuberosus*) and bread root (*Psoralea esculenta*). Its protein score is high, it is low in fat and it is a good source of starch. Of the three species, it is the highest in vitamins A and C.[50] The Indians and the members of the expedition may not have been aware of the satisfyingly high starch content, but they would have most pleased with yampa's digestibility, its pleasant flavor and its wind-dispelling quality.

•   •   •

After leaving the Bitterroot Valley, the expedition soon found itself buried in the densely forested mountains now part of western Montana and eastern Idaho. They were then west of the Continental Divide and found that the Indians relied principally on dried salmon and the roots of the plant now known as *Camassia quamash* (blue camas). The many spellings of the root

Blue camas (Camassia quamash).
Roots collected when flowers begin to wilt.

name include *quamas, kamash, kamas, camash, comas, commis* and *commas*. When made into a cake, the product was then called *pasheco, pashequaw* or *pashequa*.[51] Lewis and Clark devised many other spellings in their frequent mentions of this important root.

At Weippe Prairie in Idaho, on 20 September 1805, Clark was presented with the first sample of these roots. "Some round and much like an onion which they call *Pas she co Sweet*," he wrote. "Of this they make bread & Supe they also gave us, the bread made of this root all of which we eate hartily." Later the same day, Clark was "verry unwell all the evening from eateing the fish & roots too freely". Sergeant Patrick Gass, however, found camas bread "good and nourishing, and tastes like that sometimes made of pumpkins".[52] The next day, Clark was very sick and within a short time, most of the party also fell ill.

Captain Lewis became ill on September 24 and most of the men were complaining of a "Lax & heaviness at the stomack". The dried fish, possibly laden with bacteria, were part of the problem and the root diet did not help. The sick men were fed coyote and horse meat which alleviated the distress temporarily but by October 5, there was "Nothing to eate except dried fish & roots". That night, Clark and Lewis ate a "Supper of roots boiled, which Swelled us in Such a manner that we were Scercely able to breath for Several hours". The next respite from the fish and roots diet was furnished by dogs which, according to Gass, "when well cooked, tastes very well".[53] On October 18, they purchased 40 dogs for food and Cutright says "they reduced the dog population of the Columbia River Valley appreciably".[54]

Clark never suffered as much as Lewis and many of the men did, though he was uncomfortable much of the time during late September and early October of 1805. Lewis later wrote that camas "is pallateable but disagrees with me in every shape I have ever used it". A welcome diversion was furnished by Private John Collins on October 21 when he made some "excellent beer of the *Pasheco quarmash* bread of roots which," Clark reported, "was very good". The camas bread had become wet and moldy and apparently fermented. (Collins's fondness for alcohol had landed him in trouble earlier on the expedition. On 29 June 1804 he was found guilty of drunkenness on duty and received one hundred lashes on "his Bear Back".)

Much has been written of camas, its nutritive value, the distressing effects of over-consumption and its importance as a staple and emergency food. Cutright, a biologist, wrote that the change of diet from meat to salmon and camas roots caused the illness of Lewis ("completely incapacitated")[55] and the men. Coues, a medical doctor, stated that camas roots "seem to possess very active properties" and that they are "both emetic and purgative to those who are not accustomed to eat it".[56] Nutritionally, camas contains much sugar that is indigestible unless converted by long cooking to digestible fructose. Eaten raw or lightly cooked, as the expedition members often ate it, it can be very disagreeable. Camas was and is used as a sweet and contains little or no starch.

Because of its great abundance, camas was a food plant of much importance to interior tribes. Despite its unpleasant effects, it was of value to other explorers and early settlers. David Thompson, in 1811, found them "of a pleasant taste, easily masticated and nutritive". Some of the roots he dug in 1811 were "in good preservation" 36 years later.[57] David Douglas wrote of a Mr. Finlay and his family who, in 1826, had lived for six weeks on camas roots and black lichen in eastern Washington.[58] Hart repeats many stories illustrating the wide use of camas by Indians and by whites in the nineteenth century.[59]

The Lewis and Clark party again traded for camas roots on the return journey up the Clearwater River, over the Bitterroot Mountains and down to Travellers rest. On 11 June 1806, Lewis wrote a long and detailed description of the plant, its habitat and the method of cooking. He noted that when the Indians "have them in abundance they form an ingredient in almost every dish they prepare".

Despite his aversion to the root, Lewis was impressed by the sight of a field of camas in bloom. "the quawmash is now in blume," he wrote, "and from the colour of its bloom at a short distance it resembles lakes of fine clear water, so complete is this deseption that on first sight I could have swoarn it was water". Later travelers, as well, have been fooled by this "deseption" -- "lakes" of camas distract many motorists on highways in Idaho and Montana in early summer.

A "lake" of blue camas, Stanley, Idaho.

• • •

Another source of sugar was first tasted by expedition members on the Pacific Coast. While describing the Chinook Indians, their appearance, possessions and food habits, Clark mentioned "a black root which they call *Shaw-na-tah-que*". This was the root of the edible thistle, *Cnicus edulis* (now *Cirsium edule*). While at Fort Clatsop, Clark wrote that the crew was presented with several roots, one of which was "a black root cured in a kill like the *pash-a-co* [blue camas] above; this root has a Sweet taste and the nativs are verry fond of it". Lewis later wrote that the root was white and crisp when first collected and, in this stage, "vastly inferior". The root was prepared by long slow cooking when it became black and "more shugary than any f[r]uit or root that I have met with in uce among the natives; the sweet is precisely that of the sugar in flavor". According to Coues, the expedition members found it "most agreeable to our palates" when the cooked product was pounded fine and mixed with cold water to a kind of mush.[60]

Lewis collected the plant on 13 March 1806 at Fort Clatsop, labelling it "Carduus or Thistle-Roots, eatable".[61] Almost all samplers of edible plants list one species or another of *Cirsium* as emergency or useful food and often include young peeled stems as additional provender. Lewis J. Clark, for example, writes that "the tap root and lower stem, when peeled, provide a pleasantly-flavoured emergency food".[62]

• • •

While descending the Columbia River in November of 1805, the expedition first met with *Sagittaria latifolia,* known to the Indians as *wapato* and often called arrowhead. The plant, highly valued by the Indians of the coast and an important article of trade, was to become part of the expedition's diet while wintering at Fort Clatsop. Patrick Gass thought the roots "of a superior quality to any I had ever seen".[63]

Wapato *or arrowhead* (Sagittaria).

Clark was undoubtedly the first writer to mention the method of collection of *wapato.* ". . . the women collect by getting into the water, sometimes to their necks holding by a small canoe and with their feet loosen the wapato or bulb of the root from the bottom from the Fibers, and it imedeately rises to the top of the water . . . those deep roots are the largest and best roots". The usual method of cooking was roasting in embers until soft when, Clark wrote, it "answers verry well in place of bread". He also mentioned several times that the Indians charged "imoderate pricies" for the roots. This was due, partially at least, to the fact that the coastal Indians themselves traded with inland Indians for *wapato. Wapato* was not found on the coast but grew as close as fifteen miles inland.

The diet of lean elk and *wapato* brought the men through the wet winter at Fort Clatsop. In early spring, they supplemented their meager fare with sturgeon and "fresh Anchovies" (actually a smelt, the eulachon or candle fish, *Thaleichthys pacificus*) and, on March 11, Lewis announced "we once more live in clover; anchovies fresh Sturgeon and Wappetoe".

Though *wapato* was "never out of season,"[64] the expedition secured their last supply in early April. They then traded three bear cubs for a supply of the roots, since the Indians "fancied those pets".

Sagittaria latifolia still is found near the Pacific coast from Vancouver Island to central California. The abundance of the plant has been severely diminished since the time of Lewis and Clark and, as early as 1906, C. V. Piper stated that "the introduction of the European carp into the Columbia River has nearly caused the extermination of this plant, where it used to be abundant".[65] In more recent years, the destruction of habitat has brought on further loss. What is probably the largest remaining pure stand, about thirty acres, is on Franz Lake in western Washington and is privately owned.[66]

• • •

Lewis mentioned a few other edible roots while at Fort Clatsop, but apparently the men made scant use of them. The cat tail (*Typha latifolia*) root "is pleasantly taisted and appears to very nutricious," wrote Lewis, "it appears to me that this substance [the part separated from the fibers] would make an excellent starch; nothing can be of a purer white than it is".

Roots of two other plants, *Equiseteum telmateia* and *Pteridium aquilinum*, were eaten by coastal Indians and were often accompanied by warm blubber. *Equiseteum* (horse tail) roots were edible, but "reather insipid in point of flavour". They probably were only sampled, as were the roots of *Pteridium*, a fern. After chewing the fern root, Lewis detected an aftertaste; "this pungency was disagreeable to me, but the natives eat it very voraciously and I have no doubt but it is a very nutricious food".[67]

• • •

On the return trip in early 1806, the expedition again faced lean times as they traveled east through the valleys and snow-covered mountains toward western Montana. Just as salmon and blue camas roots fortified the men on the westward journey in 1805, the root of cous, *Lomatium cous*, became very important in 1806. Variously known as *kouse, cows, cowas, cowish, cow-weed* and *cowse*, it was known to the Indians, according to Lewis, as *shappalell*.[68] As used by the expedition and by Indians of the time, cous probably referred to the roots of several species of the genus, including *L. cous, L. macrocarpum,* and possibly *L. triternatum*. The usual treatment was to grind the dried roots into a meal and shape them into large flat cakes. The cakes were then eaten "without any further preperation" or boiled into a kind of gruel. "The latter is most common and much the most agreeable," wrote Lewis, "the flavor of the root is not very unlike the gensang". Cous

Cous or biscuitroot (Lomatium cous).

roots were collected from early spring until the time of the blue camas harvest in June when they became much less palatable.

From April to late June of 1806, many journal entries record trading for "chapellel cakes", "pieces of Chapellell", "bread of cows" and "mush of the bread of cows". On one occasion, Clark "hed to purchase 3 dogs for the men to eate & some Shap-per-lell".

Cous and blue camas were by far the most important root foods on the eastward journey, and the two were compared by Lewis. In late May, he decided that every member of the expedition should be provided with "a parsel of bread [of cous] and roots [blue camas]" for the impending mountain passage. Lewis, at least, much preferred cous to camas and when Clark was given "a few dry Quawmas roots as a great present," Lewis commented "but in our estimation those of cows are much better, I am confident they are much more healthy". Earlier, Lewis welcomed a collection of yampa roots by Sacagawea, writing, "they dispell the wind which the roots called Cows and quawmash are apt to create particularly the latter".

A problem with collecting various species of *Lomatium* was the superficial similarity with the flowers of poison hemlock (*Cicuta spp.*). As Coues stated, "the two might be confounded with disastrous results",[69] as they have been in a number of recorded cases. Yampa is also similar in appearance to *Cicuta* and known fatalities have occurred as a result of a confusion of these two roots. Lewis was aware of this danger and did not let the men collect the edible roots even when they were hungry since "we are affraid that they might poison themselves".

Blue camas also can be confused with the poisonous death camas (*Zygadenus spp.*), especially when the flowers have faded and dropped. Lewis J. Clark reports that some tribes "sedulously rogued out, during flowering time, the bulbs of Poison Camas occurring in their prized food areas"[70] since the bulbs of the two genera are so similar. Harrington states that Indians, children and livestock have been poisoned by death camas.[71] Most of the poisoning probably resulted when the Indians took the mixed roots from rodent caches, though experienced plant persons could readily distinguish them.[72] Lewis and Clark did not report the problem though the local Indians certainly knew of it. Lewis, incidentally, collected a death camas, *Zygadenus elegans*, on 7 July 1806, the first collection of that species.[73]

Upon crossing Lolo Pass on 27 June 1806, the men were down to eating bear oil mixed with boiled roots and two days later, "we were reduced to our roots alone without salt". After the expedition split up at Travellers rest, Clark traveled up the Bitterroot Valley and "scelebrated" Independence Day near the site of Corvallis, Montana. "I had every disposition to selebrate this day," he wrote, "and therefore halted early and partook of a Sumptious Dinner of fat Saddle of Venison and Mush of Cows". His last mention of the root was made two days later near the site of today's Big Hole Battlefield — "(This is the great plain where Shoshonees gather quamash & cows etc. our woman has done so. many beaver)".

Lewis's party was still eating cous in late July. On July 24, the men "have still a little bread of cows remaining of which we made a kettle of mush which together with a few pigeons ... served us with food for this day". This was the last of the cous and soon the men were feasting on fat buffalo.

Cous and blue camas were of relatively equal importance to the expedition. On the westward journey, blue camas may well have supplemented the slender rations to a necessary degree[74] though much distress accompanied their ingestion. Because of the time of year, cous replaced blue camas as the primary root food in 1806 and it apparently was easier to digest. Blue camas roots are high in sugar, low in starch, and not of exceptionally high nutritional value.[75] Cous roots contain more starch and generally would be more satisfying to active persons. Both roots occur, where they are found, in great abundance.

• • •

A number of other roots were described by Lewis. A few obviously were sampled and others simply were mentioned. *Brodiaea*, described by Lewis as a "species of hiasinth", was eaten by the Indians as was the root of sego lily (*Calochortus spp.*), "a small bulb of a pleasant flavor".[76] Glacier lily (*Erythronium grandiflorum*) was collected twice in 1806 and one collection bears Lewis's annotation "the natives reckon the root unfit for food".[77] Most modern texts consider glacier lily roots as edible, though they warn of possible emetic effects.[78]

Two species of fritillary (*Fritillaria lanceolata* and *F. pudica*) were described by Lewis as edible,[79] though he apparently did not try them. Of the confusing number of roots tasting like potatoes or sweet potatoes, *Potentilla anserina* received brief mention. Lewis's herbarium label reads, "The roots are eaten by the natives, and taste like sweet potatoes".[80] This short shrift is somewhat surprising as the plant grows in abundance in many places along the expedition's route and is, as Harrington writes, not only an "excellent food", but also "an excellent survival plant".[81] If it were recognized (which it probably was not) *Potentilla anserina* would have served the expedition well, particularly in the spring of 1806.

• • •

As much as roots may have nourished the Corps of Discovery, the men often complained of a root diet, especially when deprived of meat. Although Lewis stated that he "was always much attatched" to vegetable food, he declared that he enjoyed "the most perfect health" when the diet, at Fort Clatsop, was limited to "lean elk boiled with pure water, and a little salt". Nevertheless, he admitted that he did not feel strong on this limited fare.

Clark, who seems to have had a stronger constitution than Lewis, suffered less than his partner when the crew was struck down by the diet of salmon and blue camas roots in the fall of 1805. At Fort Clatsop, he noted that he had "become entirely cearless about my diat." In a philosophical passage, he continued, "I have learned to think that if the cord be suffiecently strong which binds the soul and boddy together, it does not so much matter about the materials which compose it".

Edible roots supplemented the portable soup (rarely mentioned and presumably no favorite), fish, birds, dog, horse, elk, deer, bear and whale consumed during the period from the late summer of 1805 to midsummer of 1806. As such, they probably did not actually save lives and, though they occasionally caused acute discomfort, they added variety to an otherwise monotonous protein diet. Nevertheless, Lewis was always suspicious of roots as food. When three men complained of "violent pains in their heads" while two others were "afflicted with the cholic," Lewis declared these illnesses were caused by "their diet of roots which they have not been accustomed".

Both Clark and Lewis commented on the effect of root consumption on the health of western Indians. Along the Columbia, Clark observed that the tribes had bad teeth that were "worn to the gums". He believed this was from eating both sandy roots and the skin and scales of salmon. Various disorders among the Chopunnish of the upper Clearwater were attributed by Lewis to "their confinement to a diet of roots". Their sore eyes, so common to all ages, were caused, he wrote, "by the state of debility incident to a vegetable diet". In May of 1806, an Indian chief was brought to Lewis and Clark for treatment. The chief was perfectly immobile, though he appeared to be in sound health. Lewis surmised that he was incapacitated "by some disorder which owed it's origine to a diet of particular roots". After bouts of enforced sweating, the chief became much better. Lewis's diagnosis, implying ingestion of some vegetable toxin, could very well have been accurate.

A final observation on the effects of a root diet still is debated by students of animal diet and behavior. The expedition had a number of encounters with the grizzlies of the upper Missouri and Lewis commented on the "farocity" of this "furious and formidable anamal". While encamped on the Upper Clearwater in May of 1806, he speculated on the differences between the Missouri and Clearwater bears. "the variagated bear," he wrote, " I beleive to be the same here with those on the missouri but these are not so ferocious as those perhaps from the circumstance of their being compelled from the scarcity of game in this quarter to live more on roots and of course not so much in the habit of seizing and devouring living animals. the bear here are far from being as passive as the common black bear they have attacked and fought our hunters already but not so fiercely as those of the Missouri".

• • •

ENDNOTES

1. Jefferson to Lewis, 20 June 1803. In Thwaites, 7, p. 247-252. Unless otherwise acknowledged, quotes by Lewis and Clark are from the *Journals*, R. G. Thwaites editor, 1969 edition.

2. Jefferson to Dr. Benjamin Rush, 28 February 1803. Thwaites, 7, p. 211.

3. Cutright, p. 26. Ronda points out that there is no proof that Lewis studied "scientific subjects". Ronda, p. 7.

4. ". . . Lewis's specimens and data are as ample, or no more inadequate, than many collections made today by persons with considerable botanical training". Rudd, p. 356.

5. While at Fort Clatsop. Quoted in Coues, III, p. 829 note.

6. Cutright, p. 19.

7. Ibid. Bernard DeVoto wrote "both were men of great intelligence, of distinguished intelligence". Introduction to Thwaites, 1, n. p.

8. Thwaites, 1, p. lvi. Elijah Criswell's comments are more detailed. "In the main, it [Lewis's style] is a grammatically correct, flowing, somewhat artificial and sophisticated eighteenth century style, abounding in elegant language, with some evidence of a grave reserved humor, and now and then a touch of sentimentality. Lewis was a rather introspective, solitary, and melancholy character, as evidenced by his habit of walking alone up the banks of the Missouri while his boats breasted the current with the forthright Clark in command", p. xix. Of Clark, Criswell wrote, "Not in the least introspective or solitary in nature, he was direct, practical, and sensible . . . Clark's style of writing, not so correct and not so polished as that of Lewis, is, nevertheless, direct, straightforward, forceful, and wholly lacking in the circumlocution to be found in Lewis's writing". Criswell, p. xxxiii.

9. Thwaites, 1, p. xxxvi.

10. Lewis's fountain is still recognizable but, as a result of cattle in the area, it is no longer "pure".

11. Steyermark, p. 668.

12. Harrington, p. 180.

13. Moulton, 2, p. 224 note.

14. Palmer, p. 405.

15. These three identifications and descriptions in Thwaites, 6, 137-140.

16. Moulton, 2, p. 225 note.

17. Thwaites, 6, p. 142 note.

18. Also known as white apple or *pomme blanche*, bread root, prairie turnip, etc. Note confusion with *Apios*, above. Identification in Thwaites, 1, p. 73 note.

19. Hart, p. 61.

20. According to Moulton, 3, p. 258 note, this is Hugh Heney (or Hene), in 1804 in the service of the North West Company. In the *Journals*, he appears as Henny, Haney and Henry.

21. Cutright, p. 373.

22. Hart, p. 38.

23. Johnston, p. 56.

24. Moulton, 3, p. 258 note.

25. Cutright, p. 54.

26. Moulton identifies this as *Allium textile*, 4, p. 28 note.

27. Coues, II, p. 435; Moulton, 4, p. 422 note.

28. Moulton, however, states definitely that it was *A. schoenoprasum*, 7, p. 31 note.

29. Coues, III, p. 1029-30; Moulton, 7, p. 312 note. *A. douglasii* may be the best of wild onions. In western Montana, it was known as the "other camas". R. Diettert File.

30. According to Moulton, this was *A. geyeri*, 7, p. 266 note.

31. Meehan, p. 42.

32. Thwaites, 3, p. 230 note.

33. Davies, p. 230 and Appendix, p. 172.

34. Coues, III, p. 824 note.

35. Hitchcock, et. al., Part 3, p. 274 but not in Meehan, 1898.

36. *L. sericeus* and *L. argenteus*. Meehan, p. 22-23.

37. Davies, p. 53.

38. Palmer, however, wrote that *G. lepidota* was eaten by northwest Indians, p. 407. He, too, may have confused *Glycrrhiza* with *Lupinus*.

39. Coues. II, p. 543-4.

40. Thwaites, 5, p. 160 note.

41. Coues, I, p. 264.

42. Moulton, 3, p. 160 note; 4, p. 18 note.

43. Moulton, 5, p. 147 note.

44. Harrington, p. 225.

45. Frémont, p. 475-6.

46. Coues, II, p. 552 note.

47. Piper, p. 14, p. 426.

48. L. Clark, p. 348.

49. Hart, p. 65.

50. Quoted in Johnston, p. 66.

51. Listed by Coues, II, p. 603-4 note.

52. Gass quote, Thwaites, 3, p. 79 note.

53. Gass quote, Thwaites, 3, p. 108 note.

54. Cutright, p. 219.

55. Cutright, p. 218.

56. Coues, II, p. 615 note.

57. However, he may have become confused between the time of sampling (1811) and when he wrote of the roots (1847). Thompson, p. 261-2.

58. Davies, p. 64.

59. Hart, p. 14-18.

60. Coues, III, p. 822.

61. Meehan, p. 33.

62. L. Clark, p. 541.

63. Quoted in Coues, II, p. 693 note.

64. According to Coues, III, p. 929.

65. Piper, p. 101.

66. Croft, p. 7. Nevertheless, Hitchcock *et. al.* report (in 1969) that *Sagittaria latifolia* is "common", 1, p. 149.

67. Palmer's comment on fern root, written in 1870, is very similar. "It has a pungency which is disagreeable to the whites, but by the aborigines is much relished, and it proves to be nutritious", p. 408.

68. Herbarium label, Meehan, p. 29.

69. Coues, III, p. 1022 note.

70. L. Clark, p. 12.

71. Harrington, p. 51.

72. R. Diettert File.

73. Cutright, p. 326, p. 423.

74. Burroughs says blue camas was the "most important" of all roots to Lewis and Clark, p. 61.

75. Harrington, p. 161.

76. Herbarium label, Meehan, p. 43.

77. Ibid.

78. L. Clark, p. 20; Johnston, p. 25; Hart, p. 24; Harrington, p. 178-9.

79. Herbarium label, Meehan, p. 44.

80. Meehan, p. 25.

81. Harrington, p. 203.

APPENDIX II

TRAVELLERS REST

Travellers rest Creek, as it was known to Lewis and Clark, was, as Elliott Coues wrote in 1893, "a very notable stream in the annals of the Expedition".[1] Unfortunately, the significant and descriptive name was soon changed and as early as 1831, the stream may have been known by some spelling variant of the current name of Lolo Creek. Pierre-Jean DeSmet called it St. Regis de Borgia in 1847 and Lieutenant John Mullan referred to it as LoLo Fork in 1854. Isaac Stevens, following Mullan, wrote it down as Lou-Lou Creek in 1855[2] and Coues listed another spelling, Lulu, in 1893. Coues also mentioned "la crique du Repos du Voyageur", the French rendition found in Lallemant's edition of Patrick Gass's journal.[3]

This was an important stream to the expedition as they followed the Indian trail along its banks in September of 1805 and again in the early summer of 1806. Lewis's first mention of the stream and the camp was made on 9 September 1805 and he wrote the names for both as "Travellers rest".[4] The creek, he continued, "is about 20 yards wide a fine bould clear running stream". Every conceivable spelling variation of Lewis's Travellers rest is found in the vast Lewis and Clark literature.

The site was truly a Travellers rest and a welcome one. Everything needed was there — good water and wood, pasture for the horses and an abundance of game. The one drawback was the abundance of "musquetoes" which, Lewis reported, "have been excessively troublesome to us since our arrival at this place". The mosquitos were a result of late spring and high water of 1806.

• • •

On their way west, Lewis took celestial observations at Travellers rest and Clark wrote "the rout which we are to prosue will pass up the Travellers rest Creek". Learning from their native guide that they soon would be in densely forested country where there was little game, they set about replenishing their slender food supply. During their stay at Travellers rest, they harvested four deer, three geese, four ducks, three "prairie fowl" (presumably grouse), a woodpecker and a beaver — better than nothing but still not much for thirty-one hungry men, one woman and an infant.

On September 12, the expedition left behind the "plain and good" road up the creek and entered the thickly timbered country near today's Lolo

Valley of Travellers rest (Lolo) Creek
at junction with Clark's (Bitterroot) River.

Pass. The report of scanty game proved true and their total take for
September 11 and 12 consisted of a single "pheasant" (probably grouse). A
very interesting observation of September 12 was the comment on peeled
pines along the trail — an early report of the use of the inner bark as food
by the Indians.

•   •   •

While at Fort Clatsop during the winter of 1805-06, "in their dismal huts
. . . living like muskrats in a hole",[5] Clark compiled a map of the westward
route of the expedition from Fort Mandan to Fort Clatsop. This was, Coues
wrote, "a masterly and consummate piece of geography"[6] particularly since
it revealed that the route west was an excellent one with the exception that,
from the Dearborn River to Travellers rest, the expedition had travelled far
from the most direct route. On their return journey they planned an overland
route from Travellers rest to the Missouri drainage via the "Road to the
Buffalo" and over what has come to be known as Lewis and Clark Pass.
From that time on, the men looked forward to their arrival at Travellers rest.
Not only would the expedition divide into two parties there, but they would
be able to rest themselves and the horses. They also knew that when they
reached Travellers rest, they would once again be in good game country.

•   •   •

After crossing the Bitterroot Mountains, during which men and horses
suffered from hunger and fatigue, the expedition reached the hot springs on

Travellers rest Creek (now Lolo Hot Springs) on 29 June 1806. Here, Lewis bathed in the main spring, lasting only nineteen minutes. "It was with difficulty I could remain this long," he wrote, "and it caused a profuse sweat." The accompanying Indian guides alternated hot baths with plunges into the icy creek "repeating this transision several times but always ending with the warm bath". There is no record if the expedition members did the same, but we can guess that they did.

On June 30, they arrived at their old camp of Travellers rest. During the course of that day, they killed six deer and Lewis noted the abundance of both species of deer as well as the presence of bighorn sheep and elk in the vicinity. Clark's comments in his weather diary of the same day reflect his relief in reaching the haven of Travellers rest. "Descended the mountain to Travellers rest leaving these tremendious mountains behind us," he wrote, "in passing of which we have experienced cold and hunger of which I shall ever remember".

Plans already had been made for the separation of the expedition into two parties. Private John Shields was put to work repairing guns, and the hunters were sent out. Thirteen deer were killed, all "large and in fine order", and the meat was jerked for future use. Footraces were run between expedition members and Indians "with various success", as Lewis reported, though John Colter, who was later to run and win a race for his life with hostile Blackfeet, must have done well.

• • •

While at Travellers rest, Lewis mentioned the twelve or more species of birds in the area. At the time, none were new to science, although two, Lewis's woodpecker (*Asyndesmus lewis*) and Clark's nutcracker (*Nucifraga columbiana*), had been first reported during the expedition's westbound journey. Lewis and Clark enthusiasts will be pleased to know that both birds still can be seen, especially in spring, in the vicinity of Travellers rest.

In his journal of July 1, Lewis gave one of his typically long and detailed descriptions, this time of the "barking Squirrel," or prairie dog (*Cynomys ludovicianus*). This social little animal no longer is found in the area.

On June 30, Lewis found what later was to be described (in 1840) as *Cypripedium montanum*, or mountain lady's slipper orchid. He recognized it as a "lady's slipper or mockerson flower" and though he described it in detail, he did not collect a specimen. Mountain lady's slippers still can be found near Travellers rest, but they are quickly exterminated near developed areas. On July 2, Lewis reported he had found "two species of native clover here, the one with a very narrow small leaf & a pale red flower". One of these was *Trifolium microcephalus*, or woolly clover, first described in the literature by Pursh in 1814 from Lewis's collection. Apparently, the plant was not reported again until it was "rediscovered" by Wally Albert in 1985.[7] Woolly clover is now listed as G5/S1 in Montana, which means that it is "demonstrably secure globally, though it may be quite rare in parts of its range, especially at the periphery" / "Critically imperiled in Montana because of extreme rarity (5 or fewer occurrences, or very few remaining individuals), or because of some factor of its biology making it especially vulnerable to extirpation from the state".[8] The other "clover" (Lewis's "one with a very narrow small leaf & a pale red flower") was thin-leaved owl clover (*Orthocarpus tenuifolius*), also described by Pursh in 1814. It still can be readily found in the area.

Bitterroot was one of two other "uncommon plants specemines of which I [Lewis] preserved" while at Travellers rest. It is a mystery why Lewis, given as he was to lengthy and closely detailed descriptions of species of plants or animals new to him,[9] dismissed the flowering bitterroot with such slight mention. Perhaps he did not find the white flower particularly attractive though by any standard, they are certainly striking.

The other "uncommon" plant was *Sedum stenopetalum*, or stonecrop, previously collected on 15 June 1806 near Weippe Prairie along the Clearwater River in Idaho. Though uncommon in appearance, this yellow stonecrop is common in occurrence in the Travellers rest area today.

While at Travellers rest, Lewis also mentioned cottonwood, ponderosa pine ("the long leafed pine forms the principal timber of the neighbourhood") and fir and larch at higher elevations. All these species are still to be seen in the area, but in much diminished numbers. Some of the larger ponderosa were mature trees in 1806 and a few still bear scars caused by stripping for the inner bark that was used for food by the Indians. Sacagawea had mentioned this practice near the Three Forks of the Missouri a year earlier.

Lewis completed his natural history observations at Travellers rest with brief mention of nine shrubs: "wild rose, service berry, white berryed honeysuckle [snowberry, *Symphoricarpos alba*], seven bark [now ninebark, *Physocarpus sp.*], elder, alder aspen [probably an alder], choke cherry and the broad and narrow leafed willow". Thomas Jefferson, incidentally, was much impressed with the snowberry. In 1813, he sent a cutting derived from Lewis's collection to a friend in Paris. "Its beauty consists in a great produce of berries of the size of currants," he wrote, "and literally is white as snow, which remain on the bush through the winter".[10]

• • •

The site of Travellers rest is commemorated by three historical markers, none, in all probability, on the exact site. The first and by far the most interesting is located on the west side of Highway 93 just north of Lolo Creek. Placed by the Daughters of the American Revolution in 1925, it is dedicated to the two captains, to Sacagawea, "Their Inspiration and Guide", and to the "brave men" (all listed) of the expedition. For some reason, only the encampment of September, 1805, is mentioned. The second marker, on the south side of Lolo Creek along the highway, is essentially accurate except for the observation that the expedition "camped at the mouth of Lolo Creek". The third marker, a bronze plaque inconspicuously and unfortunately placed behind a barbed wire fence amid a field of leafy spurge, states that the site of "Traveler's Rest" is a National Historic Landmark.

Lewis and Clark were vague on exact locations, so it is impossible to determine the site of Travellers rest from either their plotted distances or their observations of latitude. Nevertheless, clues from the writings of Lewis, Clark, Ordway, Whitehouse and Gass indicate the campsite was upstream from the present bridge over Lolo Creek on Highway 93.

Later writers are divided and confusing on the subject. Olin D. Wheeler, writing in 1904, placed the campsite at "a point on the creek near where both the main county road and the northern Pacific Railway cross the stream".[11] Ralph Space later wrote that he agreed with Wheeler that "the camp was on the south side of Lolo Creek about one mile above [?] the town of Lolo".[12] Cutright wrote that "Ralph Space places the campsite opposite the south of Sleeman Gulch about two miles up Lolo Creek from its entrance into the Bitterroot River".[13] Cutright also wrote that Space "knows more about it [the Lolo Trail] in relation to the Lewis and Clark expedition than any man who ever lived".[14] Gary Moulton, a recent commentator on the subject, writes that the campsite was "perhaps one or two miles upstream from the Bitterroot River, on the south side of the creek".[15]

With most of this in mind and armed with Clark's map from the Thwaites *Journals*, Professor H. D. Hampton and I examined the area in May of 1990. We drove west on the Mormon Creek Road from Highway 93 and received permission at the Louis Vann residence to walk along the creek to where we believed we would find the site of Travellers rest. Harold was adamant we had found the site and I admit that it looked right. Even though the area had been plowed, burned, grazed and fenced for what were probably many years, it just <u>seemed</u> right.

In early 1992, I wrote to Dr. Robert Bergantino of Butte who has meticulously traced the route of the expedition across Montana. His detailed answer gave me much to think about. After evaluating contemporary reports, considering stream morphology and employing statistical methods, Bergantino determined the median location of Travellers rest campsite to be .29 miles from the Highway 93 bridge bearing S82W. His first choice is slightly east of the median location and his second choice is slightly west. This put his preferred locations for the campsite somewhat east of the spot determined by Harold and me, but our location falls within his envelope of 95% certainty and probably on the western edge of his envelope of 68% certainty.[16]

Visiting the area again in July of 1992 and this time adding to my sources Bergantino's text and map, I drove west on the Mormon Creek Road to a steep grassy hill rising to the south. From this vantage point, I looked toward the Bitterroot River, Sleeman Gulch, the town of Lolo and, finally, to the spot we believed to be the site of Travellers rest. It still looked right even though it had become a llama pasture. A few old ranches, many modern homes and some new condominiums make up the rural landscape. The vegetation is much changed with knapweed, spurge, sunflowers and flax displacing many of the native species. But with selective exclusion by the mind's eye and with a certain amount of imagination, I could see the campsite of Travellers rest.

Travellers rest, far view.

Travellers rest, near view.

ENDNOTES

1. Coues, II, p. 590 note.

2. Jackson, *Among the Sleeping Giants*, p. 119-20.

3. Coues, <u>Ibid</u>.

4. All Lewis and Clark quotes are from the *Journals*, R. G. Thwaites editor, 1969 edition.

5. Coues, II, p. 802 note.

6. <u>Ibid</u>.

7. Hoy, p. 5.

8. Lesica and Shelly, p. 58, p. 3.

9. On this, see Cutright, p. 298-9.

10. Quoted in Cutright, p. 374.

11. Wheeler, 2, p. 77.

12. Space, p. 4-5.

13. Cutright, p. 305.

14. Cutright, p. 199.

15. Moulton, 5, p. 196 note.

16. Bergantino, 1992.

BIBLIOGRAPHY

Bakeless, John. 1968. *Lewis and Clark. Partners in Discovery.* First published 1947. William Morrow and Co., New York.

Barr, Claude A. 1983. *Jewels of the Plains.* Univ. Minn. Press, Minneapolis.

Beidleman, Richard G. 1966. Lewis and Clark -- plant collectors for a president. *Horticulture*, Vol. XLIV, #4.

Bergantino, Robert. *Atlas of Lewis and Clark Expedition.* MT Hist. Soc., Helena, MT.

Bergantino, Robert. 1992. Letter from (with enclosures).

The (Hamilton) *Bitter Root Times.* Oct. 12, 1894.

Bitter Root Valley Historical Society. 1982. Bitterroot Trails. (Authors Lena Bell, Henry Grant, Phyllis Twogood). BRVHS, Hamilton. MT.

Blankinship, J. W. 1904. A Century Of Botanical Exploration in Montana, 1805-1905: Collectors, Herbaria and Bibliography. *MT Agric. College Studies*, Vol. 1, No. 1. Pub. by the College, Bozeman.

Blankinship, J. W. & Hester F. Henshall. 1905. Common Names of Montana Plants. *MT Agric. College Studies*, Vol. 1, No. 3, Pub. by the College, Bozeman.

Broadhead, Michael J. & Paul Russell Cutright. 1981. *Elliott Coues: Naturalist and Frontier Historian.* Univ. Ind. Press, Urbana.

Brown, Annora. 1954. *Old Man's Garden.* J. M. Dent & Sons, Toronto and Vancouver.

Brown, Robert. 1986. On the Vegetable Products, Used by the North-West Indians as Food and Medicine, In the Arts, and in Superstitious Rites. *Bot. Soc. Edinburgh Trans.* 9:378-96. in An Ethnobiology Source Book. Ed. & intro. by Robert F. Ford. Garland Pub., Inc., New York & London. First pub. 1868.

Browne, J. Ross. 1868. The Mineral Resources in the States and Territories West of the Rocky Mountains. March 5, 1868. *House Exec. Doc.* No. 202, 40th Congress, 2nd Session. GPO, Washington.

Burroughs, R. D. 1966. The Lewis and Clark Expedition's Botanical Discoveries. *Nat. Hist.*, LXXV, #1.

Cappious, Samuel Lloyd. 1939. A History of the Bitterroot Valley to 1914. M.A. Thesis, Univ. Wash., Seattle.

Carrara, Paul C. 1989. Late Quaternary Glacial and Vegetative History of the Glacier National Park Region, Montana. USGS *Bull.* 1902. GPO, Washington.

Carrara, Paul C. 1986. Letter from, 26 Nov 1986.

Ciesla, Bill. 1982. Bitterroot. *MT Mag.*, Vol. 12, #6.

Clark, Ella. 1966. *Indian Legends of the Northern Rockies.* Univ. Okla. Press, Norman.

Clark, Lewis J. 1976. *Wild Flowers of the Pacific Northwest from Alaska to Northern California.* Rev. ed. by John G. Trelawny. Gray's Pub. Ltd, Sidney, B. C.

Clark, W. A. Esq. 1891. Centennial Address on the Origin, Growth and Resources of Montana, Delivered at the Centennial Exposition, Oct. 11, 1876. *Contr. to the Hist. Soc. of Mont.* Repub. by J. S. Canner & Co., Inc, Boston, 1966.

Colley, J. Cobb & Baldassare Mineo. 1985. Lewisias for the Garden. *Pac. Hort.* 46 (2): 40-49.

Coues, Elliott. 1898. Notes on Mr. Thomas Meehan's Paper on the Plants of Lewis and Clark's Expedition Across the Continent, 1804-06. *Proc. Acad. Nat. Sci. Phil.* L: 291-315.

Coues, Elliott (ed.). 1893. *The History of the Lewis and Clark Expedition By Meriwether Lewis and William Clark.* 3 vol. (Repub. Dover Pub., Inc., New York).

Criswell, Elijah Harry. 1940. Lewis and Clark: Linguistic Pioneers. *Univ. Missouri Studies*, Vol. XV, No. 2.

Croft, Roy D. 1982. Lewis and Clark's Wapato -- Endangered Plant Fights for Survival. *We Proceeded On*, Vol. 8, No. 1.

Cronquist, Arthur. 1981. *An Integrated System of Classification of Flowering Plants.* Col. Univ. Press, New York.

Cutright, Paul Russell. 1969. *Lewis and Clark. Pioneering Naturalists.* Univ. Nebr. Press, Lincoln & London.

Daubenmire, R. 1975. An ecological life-history of *Lewisia rediviva.* (Portulacaceae). *Syesis*, Vol. 8: 9-23.

Davidson, B. LeRoy. 1990. Lewisias of the Sierra Nevada. ARGS *Bull.*, Vol. 48, No. 1: 13-16.

Davies, John. 1980. *Douglas of the Forests. The North American Journals of David Douglas.* Univ. Wash. Press, Seattle.

Davis, Ray J. 1952. *Flora Of Idaho.* William C. Brown Co. Dubuque, Iowa.

Deno, Norman C. 1991. *Seed Germination, Theory and Practice.* Norman C. Deno, State College, PA.

DeSanto, Jerry. 1989. *Alpine Wildflowers of Glacier National Park, Montana and Waterton Lakes National Park, Alberta.* J. DeSanto, Columbia Falls, MT.

DeSmet, Pierre-Jean, S. J. 1978. *Oregon Missions and Travels Over the Rocky Mountains In 1845-46.* Reprint. Ye Galleon Press, Fairfield, WA.

Diettert, Reuben. c. 1950s. Diettert File. Missoula, MT.

Doonan, Stephen. 1991. Growing Wenatchee Wildflowers. ARGS *Bull.*, Vol. 49, No. 3: 193-206.

Drummond, Thomas. 1830. Sketches of a Journey to the Rocky Mountains and to the Columbia River. Ed. by Sir W. J. Hooker. *Bot. Misc.*, Vol. 1. London.

Duncan, Dayton. 1987. *Out West (An American Journey).* Viking, New York.

Elliott, R. C. 1966. The Genus Lewisia. AGS pub. Reprinted from Vol. xxxiv (1966) of AGS's *Bull.*

Elrod, Morton John. n.d. *The Lovely Bitterroot Flower.* Typewritten. UM Archives, Missoula.

Ewan, Joseph. 1952. Frederick Pursh, 1774-1820, And His Botanical Associates. *Proc. Am. Phil. Soc.*, Vol. 96, No. 5: 599-628.

Ewers, John C. 1958. *The Blackfeet. Raiders on the Northwestern Plains.* Univ. Okla. Press, Norman & London.

Farrer, Reginald. 1975. *The English Rock-Garden*. Vol. 1. First pub. 1919. Theophrastus, Sakonnet reprint.

Fernald, M. L. 1942. Some Early Botanists of the American Philosophical Society. *Proc. Am. Phil. Soc.*, Vol. 86; 63-71.

Ferris, Robert G. (ed.). 1975. *Lewis and Clark Historic Places Associated with their Transcontinental Exploration (1804-06))*. USDI, NPS, Washington.

Foster, H. Lincoln. 1982. *Rock Gardening*. Timber Press, Portland, OR.

Frémont, John Charles. 1970. *The Expedition of John Charles Frémont*. Vol. 1. Ed. by Donald Jackson & Mary Lee Spence. Univ. Ill. Press, Urbana, Chicago & London.

The Garden. 1887. An Illustrated Weekly Journal of Horticulture in All Its Branches. Vol. 31: 124-5 & Plate 582. Covent Garden, London.

Geyer, Chas A. 1846. Notes on the Vegetation and General Character of the Missouri and Oregon Territories, made during a Botanical Journey in the State of Missouri, and across the South Pass of the Rocky Mountains, to the Pacific, during the years 1843 and 1844. *London Jour. Bot.* Vol. 5: 285-310. Ed. by Sir. W. J. Hooker. Bailliere, London.

Grinnell, George Bird. 1962. *Blackfoot Lodge Tales. The Story of a Prairie People*. Reprint. Univ. Nebr. Press, Lincoln.

Harrington, H. D. 1967. *Edible Native Plants of the Rocky Mountains*. Univ. New Mex. Press, Albuquerque.

Hart, Jeff. 1976. *Montana -- Native Plants and Early People*. MT Hist. Soc., Helena, MT.

Havard, Dr. V., U. S. Army. 1895. Food Plants of the North American Indians. *Bull. Torrey Bot. Club*, Vol. 22. New York.

Heath, Royton E. 1983. *Collectors' Alpines*. First pub. 1964. Timber Press, Beaverton, OR.

Hellson, John C. & Morgan Gadd. 1974. Ethnobotany of the Blackfoot Indians. *Can. Eth. Serv. Paper No. 19* National Museum of Man Mercury Series. Ottawa.

Hills, Lawrence D. 1959. *The Propagation of Alpines*. Second edition revised. Theophrastus, Sakonnet reprint, 1976.

Hitchcock, C. Leo & Arthur Cronquist. 1973. *Flora of the Pacific Northwest*. Univ. Wash. Press, Seattle & London.

Hitchcock, C. Leo & Arthur Cronquist. 1964. *Vascular Plants of the Pacific Northwest*. Part 2. Univ. Wash. Press, Seattle & London.

Hogan, Sean. 1990. Lewisias, Wild and Cultivated. ARGS *Bull.*, Vol. 48, #1: 47-52.

Hohn, Janet E. 1975. Biosystematic studies of the Genus *Lewisia*, Section Cotyledon (Portulacaceae) Unpub. Ph. D. diss. Univ. Wash., Seattle.

Holmgren, Arthur H. 1954. A New Lewisia from Nevada. *Leaf. West. Bot.*, Vol. VII, No. 6: 135-7.

Hooker, William J. 1830. Some Observations on a North American Plant, Supposed to be the Lewisia of Mr. Pursh. *Bot. Misc.*, I:344-356.

Hooker, Sir W. J. 1836. Companion to the Botanical Magazine; A Brief Memoir of the Life of David Douglas, With Extracts From His Letters. Samuel Curtis, London.

Hooker, Sir William Jackson. 1840. *Flora Boreali-Americana*. Orig. pub. Henry G. Bohn, London. Reprint in 1960.

Hooker, William Jackson. 1863. *Curtis's Botanical Magazine*, Vol. XIX, 3rd series, Tab. 5395. Lovell Reeve & Co., London.

Hooker, William Jackson & George Arnott Walker-Arnott. 1840-41. The botany of Captain Beechey's voyage; comprising an account of the plants etc. "California Supplement," Henry G. Bohn, London.

Hoy, Judy. 1993. Rediscovering Lost Species. *Kelseya*. Vol. 6, No. 3.

Ingwersen, Will. 1983. *Alpines and Rock Plants*. J. M. Dent & Sons Ltd, London, Toronto, Melbourne.

Jackson, Donald. 1987. *Among the Sleeping Giants. Occasional Pieces on Lewis and Clark*. Univ. Ill. Press, Chicago & Urbana.

Jackson, Donald. (ed.). 1962. *Letters of the Lewis and Clark Expedition with Related Documents 1783-1854*. Univ. Ill. Press, Urbana.

Johnson, Olga Wedemeyer. (ed.). 1950. *The Story of the Tobacco Plains Country*. Caxton Printers Ltd, Caldwell, Idaho.

Johnston, Alex. 1987. Plants and the Blackfoot. *Occ. Paper #15*. Lethbridge Hist. Soc., Lethbridge, Alberta.

Kartesz, John Thomas. 1988. A Flora of Nevada. UMI, Ann Arbor.

Kearney, Thomas, Robert Peebles, et. al. 1951. Arizona Flora. Univ. Cal. Press, Berkeley & Los Angeles.

Kirkwood, J. E. 1916. The Bitter Root. *The Inter-Mountain Educator*, Vol. 11, No. 10: 45-6.

Kuijt, Job. 1989. Letter from, 19 Oct. 1989.

Kuijt, Job & Gail R. Michener. 1985. First record of the Bitterroot, *Lewisia rediviva*, in Alberta. *Can. Field-Nat.*, Vol.99 (2): 264-6.

Larrison, Earl J., Grace W. Patrick, William H. Baker & James A. Yaich. 1974. *Washington Wildflowers*. Seattle Audubon Soc., Seattle.

Lemmon, Robert S. & Charles C. Johnson. 1961. *Wildflowers of North America in Full Color*. Hanover House, Garden City & New York.

Lesica, Peter & J. Stephen Shelly. 1991. *Sensitive, Threatened and Endangered Vascular Plants of Montana*. MT Natural Heritage Program, Helena.

Lindley, John & Thomas Moore. 1889. *The Treasury of Botany: A Popular Dictionary of the Vegetable Kingdom*. New & revised ed. Part II. Longmans. Green. and Co., London & New York.

Malouf, Carling. n.d. Letter from.

Marvel, Stephen C. 1986. Ecophysiology of *Lewisia rediviva* Pursh (Portulacaceae). Unpub. Ph. D. diss., Univ. MT.

Mathew, Brian. 1989. *The Genus Lewisia*. The Royal Botanic Gardens, Kew, in assoc. with Christopher Helm and Timber Press, Portland, OR.

Mayr, Ernst. 1988. *Toward a New Philosophy of Biology. Observations of an Evolutionist*. Harvard Univ. Press, Cambridge & London.

McClintock, Walter, 1910. *The Old North Trail.* Univ. Nebr. Press, Lincoln, reprinted in 1968.

McDougall, W. B. & Herma A. Baggley. 1956. Plants of the Yellowstone National Park. YLMA, YNP, Wyo.

McKelvey, Susan Delano. 1955. *Botanical Exploration of the TransMississippi West. 1790-1850.* Arnold Arboretum, Harvard Univ., Jamaica Plains, MA.

Medsger, Oliver Perry. 1939. *Edible Wild Plants.* Reprinted 1959. MacMillan Co., New York.

Meehan, Thomas. 1898. The Plants of Lewis & Clark's Expedition Across the Continent, 1804-1806. *Proc. Acad. Nat. Sci. Phil.,* Vol. 50, ser. 3: 12-49.

Mengarini, Gregory, S. J. 1938. Memoirs of Old Oregon, 1841-1850, and St. Mary's Mission. Ed. by Albert J. Partoll. Hist. Reprints. *Sources Of Northwest History,* No. 25. MT State Univ., Missoula.

The *Missoulian.* May 5, 1929.

Montana Historical Society. Bitterroot File, 7 items.

Morfill, W. R. 1908. William Jackson Hooker. DNB, Vol. IX:1191. Smith, Elder, & Co., London.

Moulton, Gary E. (ed.). 1986. *The Journals of Lewis and Clark Expedition.* Univ. Nebr. Press, Lincoln & London.

Mourning Dove. *A Salishan Autobiography.* 1990. Ed. by Jay Miller. Univ. Nebr. Press, Lincoln & London.

Munz, Philip A. 1969. *A California Flora with Supplement.* Univ. Cal. Press, Berkeley, Los Angeles & London.

Murray, Genevieve F. Allen. 1929. The Bitterroot (*Lewisia rediviva*) in Science and In History (Montana State Flower). M.A. Thesis, Univ. MT, Missoula.

Nelson, Aven. 1912. *Spring Flora Of the Intermountain States.* Ginn & Co., Boston.

Nelson, Mrs. Marian H. 1955. The Bitterroot of Montana. Unpub. paper for Botany 534. MSU, Bozeman, MT.

Nelson, Ruth Ashton. 1969. *Handbook of Rocky Mountain Plants.* Skyland Publishers. Estes Park, CO.

Nuttall, Thomas. 1818. *The Genera of North American Plants.* Intro. by Joseph Ewan to facsimile of 1818 edition. Hafner Pub. Co., New York, 1971.

Nuttall, Thomas. 1834. A Catalogue of a Collection of Plants Made Chiefly in the Valleys of the Rocky Mountains or Northern Andes, Towards the Sources of the Columbia River, by Mr. NATHANIEL B. WYETH, and described by T. NUTTALL. Read February 18, 1834. *Jour. Acad. Nat. Sci. Phil.*

Olmsted, Gerald W. 1986. *Fielding's Lewis and Clark Trail.* Wm. Morrow Co., Inc., New York.

Palmer, Dr. Edw. 1871. Food Products of the North American Indians. *Report of the Commissioner of Agriculture For the Year 1870.* GPO, Washington.

Parizek, Bedrich. 1986. Some Experience Breeding Lewisia. ARGS *Bull.,* Vol. 44, No. 4: 193-7.

Parry, C. C., Botanist. 1871. Report of Botanist. *Report of the Commissioner of Agriculture for the Year 1870.* GPO, Washington.

Pennell, Francis W. 1950. Historic Botanical Collections of the American Philosophical Society and the Academy of Natural Sciences of Philadelphia. *Proc. Amer. Phil. Soc.* Vol. 94: 137-151.

Pichette, Pierre (narrator). 1974. *Coyote Tales of the Montana Salish*. Ed. by Harriet Miller and Elizabeth Harrison. Mus. of the Plains Indians and Crafts Center, Browning, MT.

Piper, Charles V. 1906. Flora of the State of Washington. Vol. XI. *Contr. from the U. S. Nat. Herb.* GPO, Washington.

Porteous, Barry. 1992. Rock Gardening in Ontario. ARGS *Bull.*, Vol. 50, #1: 51-57.

Porter, C. L. 1972. *A Flora of Wyoming*. Part 7. Univ. Wyo., Laramie, WY.

Purdy, Carl. 1932. New Species of Lewisia. *Leaf. West. Bot.*, Vol. 1, No. 3: 20-21.

Pursh, Frederick. 1812. Letter to Aylmer [sic] Bourke Lambert, Esq., London, 20 January 1812. "Society Papers" Collection, General Minute Book 1, p. 269, The Linnean Society of London.

Pursh, Frederick. 1814. *Flora Americae Septentrionalis; or, A Systematic Arrangement and Description of the Plants of North America. Containing, Besides What May Have Been Described By Preceding Authors; Many New And Rare Species, Collected During Twelve Years Travel And Residence in that Country.* 2 vol. with 24 engravings. Printed For White, Cochrane, and Co., London.

Range Plant Handbook. Prepared by Forest Service, USDA. 1937. GPO, Washington.

Ronda, James P. 1992. 'A Knowledge of Distant Parts.' The Shaping of the Lewis and Clark Expedition. *MT Mag. West. Hist.*, Vol. 41 (4): 4-18.

Ross, Alexander. 1956. *The Fur Hunters of the Far West*. Ed. by Kenneth A. Spaulding. Univ. Okla. Press, Norman.

Rudd, Velva E. 1954. Botanical Contributions of the Lewis and Clark Expedition. *Jour. of the Wash. Acad. Sci.*, Vol. 44, No. 11: 351-6.

Saunders, Charles Francis. 1933. *Western Wild Flowers and Their Stories*. Doubleday, Doran & Co., Inc., Garden City.

Schaeffer, Claude. 1940. *The Subsistence Quest of the Kutenai.* Unpub. Ph. D. diss., Univ. Penn.

Scotter, George W. 1990. Letter from, 9 March 1990.

Scriver, Bob. 1990. *The Blackfeet. Artists of the northern Plains*. Lowell Press, Inc., Kansas City.

Shaw, K. & L. 1992. Letter from.

Space, Ralph S. c.1970. *The Lolo Trail: a history of events connected with the Lolo Trail since Lewis and Clark*. Printcraft Printing, Lewiston, ID.

Stevensville Historical Society. 1971. *Montana Genesis*. Mountain Press Pub. Co., Missoula.

Steyermark, Julian A. 1963. *Flora of Missouri*. ISU Press, Ames, Iowa.

Stone, Arthur L. 1913. *Following Old Trails*. Morton J. Elrod, Missoula.

Stuart, Granville. 1865. *Montana As It Is*. C. S. Westcott & Co., New York.

Stubbs, Ron D. 1966. An Investigation of the Edible and Medicinal Plants Used By the Flathead Indians. M.A. Thesis, Univ. MT, Missoula.

Teit, James A. 1930. Ethnobotany of the Thompson Indians of British Columbia. Ed. by Elsie Viault Steedman. Bureau of American Ethnology, *Ann. Rep.* #45, 1927-8. GPO, Washington.

Thompson, David. 1971. *Travels in Western North America to 1784-1812.* Ed. by Victor G. Hopwood. Macmillan of Canada. Toronto.

Thwaites, Reuben Gold (ed.) 1969. *Original Journals of the Lewis and Clark Expedition 1804-1806.* Orig. Pub. Dodd. Mead & Co. 1904. Arno Press, New York.

Tidestrom, Ivan. 1925. Flora of Utah and Nevada. *Contr. from the U. S. Nat. Herb.*, Vol. 25. GPO, Washington.

Torrey, John and Asa Gray M.D. 1838-40. *A Flora of North America.* 2 vol. Wiley & Putnam, New York.

True, Rodney H. 1928. Some Neglected Botanical Results of the Lewis and Clark Expedition. *Proc. Amer. Phil. Soc.*, Vol. 67, No. 1: 1-19.

Turner, Bill. 1987. Salish Indians honor bitterroot as first fruit. *Ronan Pioneer*, May 6, 1987.

Turney-High, Harry Holbert. 1933. Cooking Camas and Bitterroot. *Sci. Monthly*, XXXVI: 262-3. Reprint.

Turney-High, Harry Holbert. 1937. *The Flathead Indians of Montana.* Amer. Anthro. Assoc., Menasha, WI.

Turney-High, Harry Holbert. 1941. *Ethnography of the Kutenai.* Amer. Anthro. Assoc., Menasha, WI.

Vanderburg, Lucy. 1991. Interview, 17 May 1991.

Walker, Deward E. Jr. 1978. *Indians of Idaho.* Univ. Idaho Press, Moscow.

Watson, Sereno. 1871. Botany. Report of the U. S. Geological Exploration of the Fortieth Parallel, Clarence King, Geologist. *Prof. Papers Eng. Dept.*, U. S. Army, No. 18. GPO, Washington.

Watson, Sereno. 1875. Descriptions of New Plants. *Proc. Amer. Acad. Arts & Sci.*, 10.

Weber, Byron. 1984?. 1985 Calendar of Natural History. Mt. Lolo Hist. Soc., Lolo, MT.

Weber, William A. 1987. *Colorado Flora: Western Slope.* Colo. Assoc. Univ. Press, Boulder, CO.

The (Hamilton) *Western Times*. June 12, 1958.

Wheeler, Olin D. 1904. *The Trail of Lewis and Clark, 1804-1904.* 2 vol., G. P. Putnam's Sons, New York & London.

Wiley, Leonard. 1968. *Rare Wild Flowers of North America.* By author, Portland OR,

Williams, Kim. 1972. Petal Pushing. The *Missoulian*, June 18, 1972.

Williams, Kim. n.d. Bitterroots babied. The *Missoulian*, n.d.

Wilson, Michael C. 1990. Letter from, 31 July 1990.

Wilson, Michael Clayton, Leonard V. Hills, Brian O. K. Reeves & Stephen A. Aaberg. 1988. Bitterroot, *Lewisia rediviva*, in southwestern Alberta: cultural versus natural dispersal. *Can. Field-Nat.*, 102 (3): 515-522.

Index